MW00379927

Antenna Design

Antenna Design

A Practical Guide

George J. Monser

McGraw-Hill

New York San Francisco Washington, D.C. Auckland Bogotá
Caracas Lisbon London Madrid Mexico City Milan
Montreal New Delhi San Juan Singapore
Sydney Tokyo Toronto

Library of Congress Cataloging-in-Publication Data

Monser, George J.
Antenna design : a practical guide / George J. Monser.
p. cm.
Includes index.
ISBN 0-07-042843-3 (hc)
1. Antennas (Electronics)—Design and construction—Handbooks, manuals, etc. I. Title.
TK7871.6.M658 1996
621.382'4—dc20 95-53972
CIP

McGraw-Hill

A Division of The ***McGraw-Hill*** *Companies*

1 2 3 4 5 6 7 8 9 0 DOC/DOC 9 0 1 0 9 8 7 6

ISBN 0-07-042843-3

The sponsoring editor for this book was Steve Chapman, the editing supervisor was Fred Bernardi, and the production supervisor was Suzanne Rapcavage. It was set in Century Schoolbook by Ron Painter of McGraw-Hill's Professional Book Group composition unit.

Printed and bound by R. R. Donnelley & Sons Company.

This book is printed on recycled, acid-free paper containing a minimum of 50% recycled de-inked fiber.

To Dorothy, my life companion, and to those that followed: George, Richard, Dotilyne, William, Steven, and Susan—who believed that I could and should write a book.

Contents

Preface

This book was written to bridge the gap between Maxwell's equations and the art of antenna design. It does not pretend to survey the whole field, rather it proposes to briefly give the principal requirements and act as a guide for antenna design.

We provide a method for selecting antennas that details and discusses the requirements that may be imposed upon the antenna. Examples are used to indicate design choices for a variety of environments and packages, moving forward through analysis, paper design, breadboarding, and testing. A brief discussion of paper design vs computer modeling (and its pitfalls) is included.

As the design progresses we illustrate how tolerances can be trimmed or loosened for production and show the value of knowing when this can be done.

Knowing how to validate the design before releasing it for design and fabrication are essential to fulfilling time and cost constraints. By detailing the testing and depth of test to validate the first model, we find the critical points in the design. Once tested, we show, by example, how to analyze the test results to provide a basis for trimming or modifying the antenna, following with the trimming process and an example illustrating key points.

Next, we describe the evaluation of the prototype, avoidance of costly production pitfalls, and production of the design.

At this point the antenna engineer would meet the industrial engineer and learn about the antenna production problems. Phases of production, from testing of the first production model through procedures useful in production, are devised and discussed. The need for low-cost, positive testing is shown with an example.

The conceptual approach for sorting and creating a new antenna is illustrated. Reasons for patenting and the way to prepare a disclosure are discussed.

Throughout the text hard models were used rather than computer models so that installation effects could be included. In contrast, computer models require rigorous formulation, a supercomputer, and free-space conditions. The solution has built-in uncertainties. Anything not included in the model is a potential source of uncertainty.

Many fine engineers have helped me during my 40 years of practice with their knowledge, expertise, and encouragement. Many support personnel along the way have given me invaluable practical advice. I have attempted to collect as much of that knowledge and advice as possible into one volume in a cogent and usable manner.

To the degree that I have succeeded, I have made some small repayment to their generosity to me.

George J. Monser

Acknowledgments

I would like to acknowledge Dr. Paul Mayes and the many antenna engineers that contributed to my understanding of antennas and their firm belief that there is no substitute for a working model to support the design. I am indebted to Dr. Henry Jasik for his many contributions and early guidance in understanding the art of antenna design and practice. I would like to thank my typist, Debra L. Domke, who went far beyond being a typist, and my illustrator, Roy Hollister, who took my rough art and created the fine illustrations.

I would like to thank the Raytheon Company for the use of the many photographs which form such an important part of this book and the understanding of antennas. I would also like to thank Dr. Mayes for contributing the Foreword which serves to keynote the text. In addition, I would like to thank AEL Industries Inc. for the antenna shown to introduce the text. Finally, I would like to thank Steve Chapman, my editor, for guidance and encouragement during the preparation of the book.

Foreword

Few electrical engineering graduates have had a course about antennas. Those who have were likely introduced to various methods of theoretical analysis and to a smattering of design techniques. An engineer who is accustomed to designing circuits by using computer simulations may expect to use a similar approach with antennas. But the analysis of an antenna model is rarely accurate enough to use for evaluation of a physical antenna in its operating environment. While electromagnetics simulation programs at the present state of development may be helpful in the initial stages of antenna design, performance evaluations must still rely heavily upon empirical procedures that are not widely presented in the available publications.

This book is meant to provide neophyte antenna engineers with assistance in the vital areas of design and testing. Many years of experience in these disciplines have been capsulized for easy reference. This material is a very useful adjunct to antenna textbooks and handbooks and it should be used in conjunction with them.

Welcome to the fascinating world of antenna engineering. Have fun!

Paul E. Mayes
Urbana, Illinois

List of Abbreviations

A	Area
c	Velocity of light in free space
C	degrees Celsius
D.G.	Directive gain (computed)
E.G.	Element gain
F	Frequency
I	Current
mil	1/1000th of an inch
R	Resistance
$\times$	Multiplication
V	Voltage
Z	Impedance
Z_o	Characteristic impedance
$-$	Minus sign
$+$	Plus sign
Ω	Ohms
π	Pi (value is approximately 3.1416)
j	Operator to designate reactance
η	Efficiency
kHz	Kilohertz
MHz	Megahertz
HF	High frequency
UHF	Ultra high frequency
VHF	Very high frequency
λ	Wavelength
VSWR	Voltage standing wave ratio
c.p.s.	cycles per second
kW	Kilowatts (1000 watts)

Antenna Design

VHF conical log spiral (author's design). (*Courtesy AEL Industries Inc.*)

Chapter

1

Introduction

The purpose of this book is threefold. First, it illustrates, by example, the antenna design process. Second, it serves as a guide in translating the antenna from an engineering model to production. Third, it shows how to avoid design pitfalls. This book should give the system engineer, the antenna engineer, and the production supervisor a better understanding of antennas.

Antennas are unique in electromagnetic systems, for they form the only link between free-space and the system. And, because the system can be either a transmitting or receiving unit, the design disciplines may differ, but system performance will depend upon how well the antennas perform. Installation effects upon performance must be anticipated, for final acceptance may be based upon installed performance.

Figure 1.1 shows a typical shipboard installation (one side of the ship). There, at least five systems with antennas are displayed. Many potential obstacles are also shown.

Figure 1.2 shows an under-aircraft installation mounted on a test range. Here, in the forward pod, the forward-looking system has a clear view. The aft-looking antennas face various obstacles.

Figure 1.3 shows a mock-up for testing a wing-installed antenna system.

Chapter 2 presents a brief tutorial on how antennas work. Next, a logical grouping of antennas according to their characteristics is given in Chapter 3. Chapter 4 shows how to select an antenna as a starting point in design. Design examples are given in Chapter 5 illustrating the design process. Validating, trimming, and the final validation of the design are covered in Chapters 6 through 8. Chapter 9 points out the

Figure 1.1 Shipboard installation, one side of ship. (*Courtesy of U.S. Navy*)

pitfalls to be avoided in the design. First model tests and analyzing test results are covered in Chapters 10 and 11. Adding an extension to the antenna and other means for providing circular polarization (a special case of elliptical polarization) are described in Chapter 12. Chapters 13 through 16 describe how to anticipate and work with production to assure a good production yield. In Chapter 17, adapting to fit a constrained-space system design is illustrated. Chapter 18 presents a few reported but unproven designs showing corrective procedures. In Chapter 19, a description on how to patent your new antenna is given.

Appendix A shows how to set up and conduct RF power testing. The way to use ANA data to determine active VSWR is given in Appendix B. How to calibrate a broadband gain standard is described in Appendix C. Design details for the meanderline polarizer (used to form circular polarization) is given in Appendix D. Appendix E illustrates how to establish production tolerances. Appendix F gives the reasons for the apparent changes in beam patterns in going from linear drive (receive) to nonlinear drive (transmit). Appendix G elabo-

Figure 1.2 Underside aircraft system on test range. (*Courtesy of U.S. Air Force*)

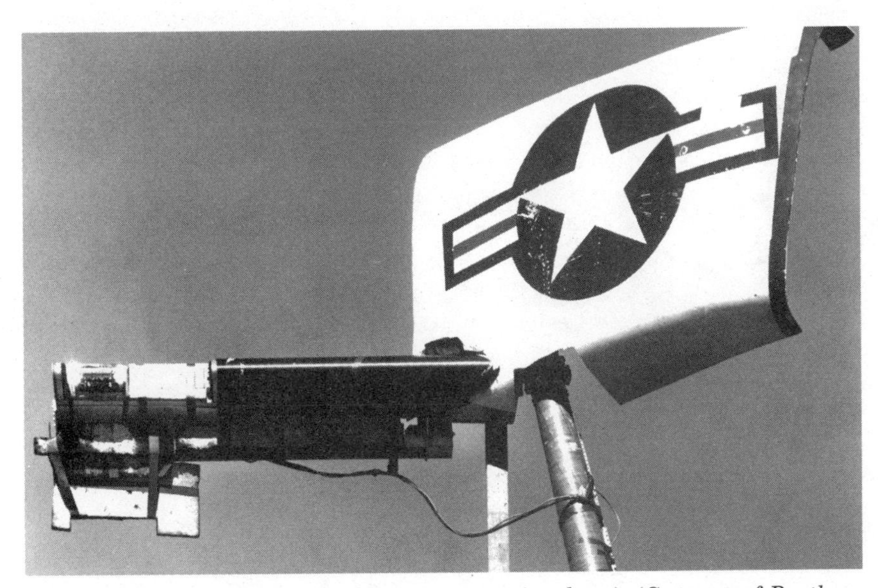

Figure 1.3 Wing-installed antennas, test range (mock-up). (*Courtesy of Raytheon Company*)

rates the patent process. Appendix H is provided to illustrate design versatility. Several antenna variants are given along with design details for the microwave array design example.

Throughout the text and appendices, solutions to the various antenna problems are developed using hard models contrasted with the method of moments, computer models. Hard models were deemed as the most expeditious solution for complex installations where the environment can, and generally does, affect the performance. In contrast, the computer model using the method of moments requires rigorous formulation, a super computer, and free-space conditions; even then the solution will have built-in uncertainties, for anything that is not in the model is a potential source of uncertainty. However, wire antennas, frequently used in HF, are better modeled on the computer where scaling all dimensions does not pose any problems.

This book focuses on VHF, UHF, and microwave antenna design and extends the concepts to other bands.

Chapter

2

How Antennas Operate

2.1 Introduction

Antennas are used as the first or last element in a system in which the antenna acts as a transducer between confined and unconfined electromagnetic energy. The confinement consists of either coaxial, two-wire, or waveguide transmission.

The radiated field, which results from discontinuities in the transmission path, is composed of two components: an electric field and a magnetic field. These fields are orthogonal in space and propagation is normal to the plane defined by these fields (Fig. 2.1).

For an antenna to act as a receiver, an electromagnetic field impinges on the antenna, which may take a variety of forms. For lower frequencies (commonly below 1000 MHz), wire antennas as a class respond to the incident field and develop a voltage across their termi-

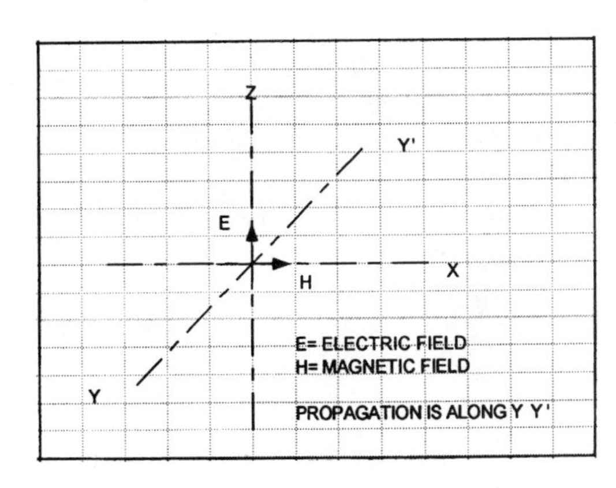

Figure 2.1 E- and H-fields orthogonal in space.

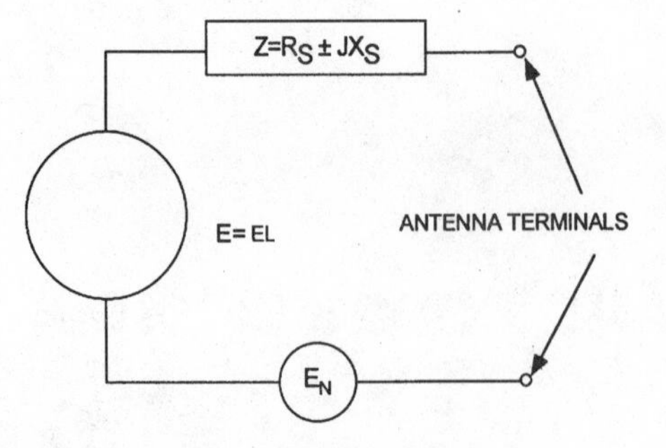

Figure 2.2 Receive antenna equivalent circuit.

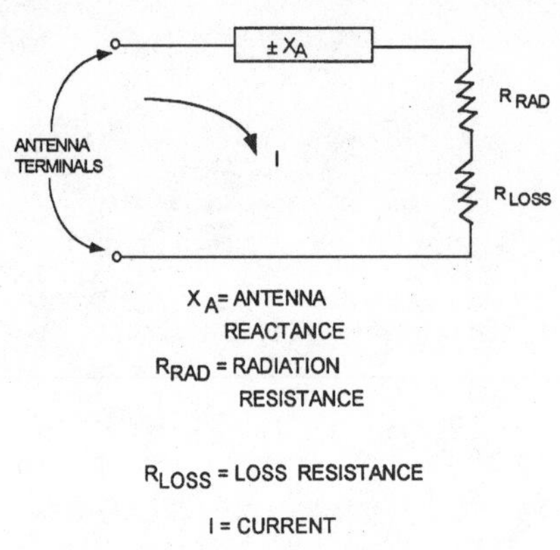

Figure 2.3 Transmit antenna equivalent circuit.

nals proportional to their electrical length. The wire antenna is further defined in terms of its impedance. The equivalent circuit (Fig. 2.2) is used to analyze receiving antenna performance, including power transfer and system noise.

For higher frequencies (commonly above 1000 MHz), aperture antennas are viewed as intercepting a portion of the incident field proportional to their capture area that is directly related to the gain.

For an antenna to act as a transmitter, the confined, propagating electromagnetic energy encounters some form of discontinuity resulting in a radiating field. For wire antennas, the discontinuity is the feed terminal, and the antenna structure loads the terminal as an impedance. The equivalent circuit (Fig. 2.3) is used to analyze radiating antenna performance.

For aperture antennas, the propagating electromagnetic energy flows through the aperture plane yielding a radiated field proportional to the antenna aperture and gain. Since the impedance at the aperture plane differs from the free-space impedance, a part of forward-flowing energy is retained by the antenna (i.e., reflected back toward the signal source).

2.2 Receive Antennas

Consider Fig. 2.2, which shows the equivalent circuit for analyzing electrically small receive antennas. In this figure, the voltage source represents the voltage developed as the product of the incident electric field and the electrical height of the antenna. For example, the electrical height of a short whip antenna is one-half its physical length and, for a loop antenna, it is proportional to the number of turns in the loop and the area defined by the loop (Bond, 1944). The impedance represents the passive load determined by the complex ratio of V and I as a transmission device.

Given the equivalent circuit for the antenna, analysis of power transfer is readily accomplished. For example, maximum power transfer occurs when the impedance added to the antenna terminals is a conjugate match to the antenna source impedance (i.e., $R_S = R_L$ and $X_S = -X_L$).

R_S, the source resistance, is composed of a loss resistance, R_g, and a radiation resistance, R_r. Both values are found by considering the antenna in the transmitting mode (described later in this book). And since R_g is a loss component, it further reduces the available power from the source.

As the antenna dimensions approach or exceed one-half wavelength, the equivalent circuit concept is generally set aside and the antenna is treated in terms of its capture area $A = (\lambda^2 G/4\Pi)$.

Given the capture area and the impinging power density on the aperture, the product yields the power available from the antenna. Analysis of power forwarded to the next component is straightforward.

2.3 Transmit Antennas

Consider Fig. 2.4, which shows the equivalent circuit for analyzing electrically small transmit antennas. In this figure, the antenna impedance, Z_A, is the ratio of the complex V and I and can be written in terms of R_A and X_A.

R_A is the antenna resistance. It is equal to the sum of R_g, the loss resistance, and the radiation resistance, R_r. R_g represents all dissipative elements within the antenna. R_r is the radiation resistance, represent-

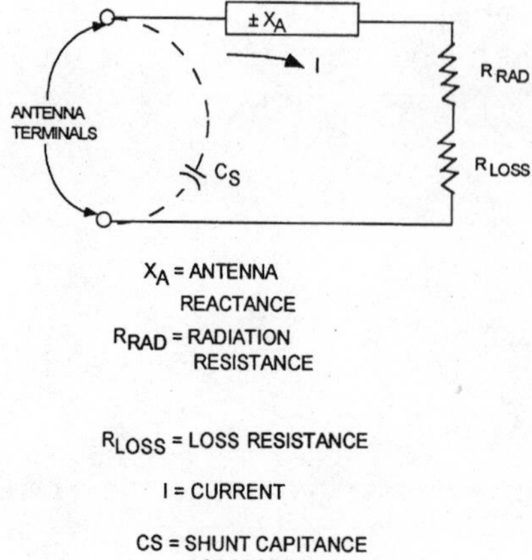

Figure 2.4 Transmit antenna equivalent circuit (detailed).

ing the conversion of input power to radiated power ($I^2 \times R_r$). Measuring the input current and radiated power, the antenna radiation resistance can be found. Here, it is standard practice to measure the far-field intensity and compute power by noting (1) that 1 kW of input power yields 186 mV/m at a distance of one mile from the source for a [(1/4)λ] vertical monopole and (2) that power is proportional to E^2.

Reference

Bond, D. S., *Radio Direction Finders,* McGraw-Hill, New York, 1944.

Chapter

3

Grouping Antennas

Antennas can be grouped as follows:

Power handling

Bandwidth

Frequency range

Coverage

Gain

Steering

Environment

Polarization

3.1 Power Handling

The power-handling requirements coupled with the environment are instrumental factors in determining elements in the design. For example, if significant power levels are to be handled, then the choice of input connector, the separation between the feed points (for balanced feeds), the decision on whether to use waveguide or wire-type radiating structures, and the avoidance of lossy materials are all important.

The power handling of the input connector is first considered. In published information such as MIL-HDBK-216, various coaxial connectors are given along with their rated root mean square (rms) voltage and suggested maximum frequency of use. However, no information is given on the power handling of the connectors. Instead, information on power handling is given for various coaxial cables intended for use with the appropriate connector type. From the handbook, the rms safe voltage can be used as a guide in determining the peak or pulse power handling of the connector. However, it must be regarded as a guide because it is based upon a low-frequency (typically 60 cycle) test under prescribed test conditions. Power breakdown at microwave frequencies differs. It is sensitive to the frequency, the environment, and the *voltage standing wave ratio* (VSWR) at the connector.

Determining a suitable connector for the continuous-wave or average power poses a problem. Certainly, the average power handling of the cable to be used with the connector can be used as a guide, with ambient and center-conductor temperature and load VSWR used to establish the cable rating. The power handling must then be derated for higher temperatures, VSWRs, and altitude. The recommended cable manufacturer's derating factors, or preferably, factors based upon test (if available) may be used.

Next, consider the impact of power handling on the separation of the feed points in balanced feeds. Voltage breakdown, as discussed earlier, determines the minimum spacing between feed points. This spacing, expressed as a fraction of a wavelength, can be used to find the smallest wavelength or maximum frequency. For example, if the minimum spacing is equal to $\lambda/8$, then a maximum f can be determined ($f = c/\lambda$). In computing f, the dimensions of c, the velocity of light, and λ, the wavelength, must be consistent.

3.2 Bandwidth

The antenna bandwidth requirement determines the antenna type. Three categories of classification exist: under half an octave, on the order of half an octave, and greater than an octave.

Under half an octave, the antenna structure is generally tuned to achieve optimum performance over the band. For requirements on the order of half an octave, the structure should be optimized to achieve the best average over-the-band performance (center band is not quite optimum). For requirements greater than an octave, some form of frequency-independent antenna is generally used. In a frequency-independent antenna, each segment (containing three to five elements) of the antenna structure is made electrically identical over any segment of the band. Only at band edges does the finite-size structure fail to be electrically identical to the adjacent segments.

3.3 Frequency Range

The frequency range determines the antenna type because it relates wavelength directly to antenna size. Antennas below 1000 MHz are usually not waveguide structures, in which the electromagnetic wave flows and smoothly radiates; rather, such antennas are some other type, in which the current distribution along the structure determines the far-field intensity.

Waveguide structures are not commonly used below 1000 MHz, because the waveguide dimensions become large and unwieldy. Also, waveguide is limited to about half an octave bandwidth. Over the frequency interval of 100 to 1000 MHz, it is practical to make the antenna at least one-half wavelength in size at the lowest frequency that yields efficient designs.

Below 100 MHz, it is less common to find antenna dimensions on the order of one-half wavelength. With decreasing frequency, the antenna becomes only a fraction of a wavelength in size. To realize an efficient transfer of power from the antenna to free-space, the structure must be made to self-resonate or an auxiliary (tuning) structure must be used. Here, the bandwidth (Δf) is determined by the antenna Q since $Q = f/\Delta f$. For the electrically small structure, the Q's become quite large and the bandwidths become small. Since $Q = X/R$, increasing R by adding some form of dissipative element yields more bandwidth. However, the added loss decreases the fraction of power radiated (reduces efficiency).

3.4 Coverage

The coverage requirement uniquely classifies the antennas. As the spatial coverage decreases, the antenna's electrical size must increase. Thus, an upper limit in the size is set by the minimum allowable spatial coverage. For example, for aperture-type antennas, the beamwidth is roughly 60 λ/w, where λ is the wavelength and w is the aperture dimension. For unity λ/w, the spatial coverage is $60° \times 60°$ (based upon the one-half power beamwidths). As w becomes greater than λ, the coverage decreases.

For $\lambda/2$ dipole antennas, coverage is 360° about the dipole and 72° (in any plane containing the dipole (half-power limits). As the length of the dipole approaches one wavelength, coverage in the plane of the dipole decreases to 47°.

When a director and reflector are added to the single $\lambda/2$ dipole, the effective aperture is increased and the beam becomes directional.

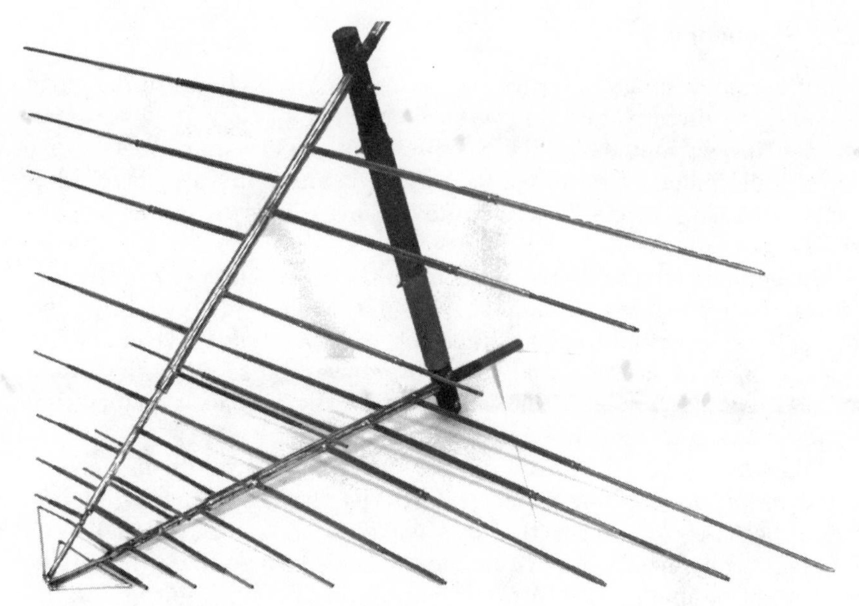

Figure 3.1 Pyramidal log-periodic antenna (test model). (*Note:* See Appendix I for additional details.)

Figure 3.1 shows a photograph of one type of frequency-independent antenna, a pyramidal log-periodic antenna. The upper frequency radiation (reception) occurs due to the smaller elements near the apex. As the frequency is lowered, the operating region creates a smooth transition to the larger elements away from the apex.

For frequency-independent antennas, the antenna's structural pattern is repeated. Thus, for any particular frequency in the band, three to five elements are effective. As the frequency is moved to another value, three to five elements are again effective and electrically identical to the first set of elements. This pattern of behavior is repeated over and over to cover the full band.

3.5 Gain

Antennas can also be grouped into low, medium, and high gain. Gain relates to how well the radiated energy is directed through a selected surface area on the spherical surface enclosing the antenna. The beamwidths through which radiation occurs are determined by the antenna dimensions in each of the two directions (Fig. 3.2), i.e., by $K_1(\lambda/W)$ and $K_2(\lambda/H)$. Here, the minimum value of $K = 50.8$ corre-

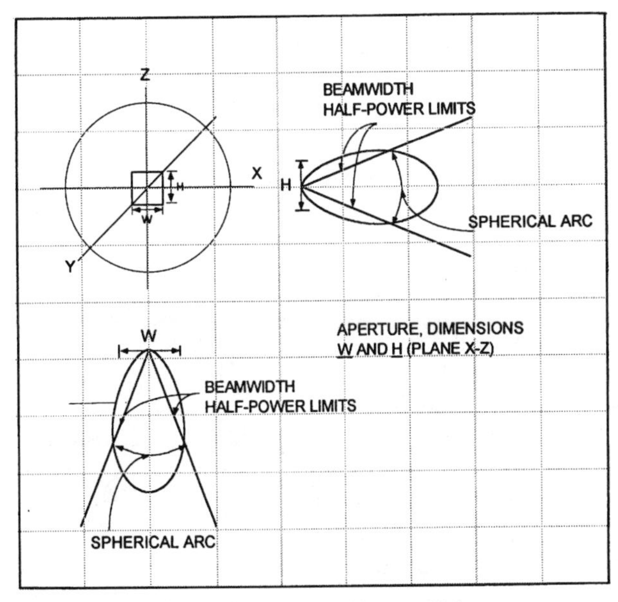

Figure 3.2 Antenna dimensions and beamwidths.

sponds to uniform in-phase current distribution. The directive gain (D.G.) is found by

$$\text{D.G.} = \frac{4\Pi A}{\lambda^2} \tag{3.1}$$

where A = the aperture area of the antenna
λ = the wavelength = c/f
c = the velocity of light
f = the operating frequency
$\Pi \cong 3.1416$

The directive gain is also approximately

$$\text{D.G.} = \frac{41{,}253}{\theta \cdot \phi} \tag{3.2}$$

where

$$\theta = K_1 \frac{\lambda}{W} \qquad \text{beam aligned with } W \tag{3.3}$$

and

$$\phi = K_2 \frac{\lambda}{H} \qquad \text{beam aligned with } H \qquad (3.4)$$

for which K_1 and K_2 are each approximately 60.

Thus the gain is set by the antenna dimensions, which are in turn limited in maximum values by the specified minimum allowable spatial coverage [see equations (3.3) and (3.4)].

3.6 Steering

The preceding paragraph showed that for a given spatial coverage, a certain gain resulted. In some applications, a higher gain is required. For these instances, some method of repositioning or moving the beam over the spatial coverage is required. Single beam repositioning can be accomplished by electromechanical means in milliseconds. In the event that faster repositioning is required, then some form of phased-array beams is required. Basically, there are two types of phased-array. One type has predetermined beam positions, each set by changing the built-in phase shifters or delay lines. The other type consists of multiple beams, in which steering is accomplished by a multithrow switch and the speed is set by the switch. Where program-controlled phase shifters are used to steer the beam, two types of phase shifters are available, diodes and ferrites.

3.7 Environment

The environment plays a role in grouping antennas. For example, in situations where severe shock and vibration exist, the antenna structure must be designed to avoid cantilever effects that could result in failure.

In installations subject to moisture or other contaminants, antenna structures that could trap moisture or contaminants should be avoided.

High-temperature environments limit the choice of dielectric materials that can be used.

3.8 Polarization

Antennas can be grouped according to whether they are linearly or elliptically polarized. For linear polarization, the E-field is predominantly in one plane. For elliptical polarization, significant E-fields exist in two orthogonal planes. Some common elliptically polarized antennas are listed in Table 3.1.

TABLE 3.1 Some Common Elliptically Polarized Antennas

Conical helix	Planar log-spiral	Conical log-spiral
Planar archimedean spiral	Hybrid-fed dual polarized notches (and similar units)	Turnstile dipoles
Helix		

Note: The planar antennas are all cavity-backed to provide a single-lobe pattern.

In addition to this grouping, a subset can be given where two orthogonal antennas, fed in phase quadrature, form elliptical polarization. A special case exists when the amplitudes are equal and the phasing is exactly 90° (i.e., circular polarization).

3.9 Summary

The preceding sections illustrate that antennas can be grouped according to various sorting criteria. These sorting factors can be arranged in descending order of importance and used to help determine antenna selection.

Chapter

4

Selection of Antennas

4.1 Introduction

There are three steps in the selection process. Step 1 is to take the system specification and translate it into an antenna requirement; step 2 is to develop a group of candidate antennas; and step 3 is to find the best candidate of the group to use for the final selection.

4.2 The System Specification

The system specification can be very detailed with regard to the antenna. In this case, translation to the antenna requirement is a straightforward process. However, if the system specification is not very detailed with regard to the antenna, interior tradeoffs can be made between the other components of the system and the antenna.

Upon completion of this task, a set of requirements should exist showing:

Frequency and spatial coverage

Power handling

Gain

Input VSWR

Polarization

Installation space

Operating environment

Storage environment

The first five items listed are performance requirements. Installation space, which determines the antenna size, requires analysis of the system mechanical package and the platform in which the system will be used. The system mechanical package can be established from the system block diagram and preliminary design of the building blocks.

The platform poses unique problems. Drawings detailing the space are frequently hard to acquire. Also, information on the other equipment sharing the installation space is even more difficult to acquire. Platform modifications documented in technical orders have limited distribution. Finally, the radome associated with the platform needs to be assessed for compatibility with the new system.

4.3 The Selection Process

Four examples of the selection process are given. Example 4.1 illustrates a transmit application covering 100 to 500 MHz. Example 4.2 illustrates a transmit application covering 5.0 to 17.0 GHz. Examples 4.3 and 4.4 cover the receive antennas for Examples 4.1 and 4.2.

Example 4.1 An antenna is to be selected to satisfy the following transmit requirements over the 100 MHz to 500 MHz frequency range:

1. VSWR = 2/1, referenced to a 50-Ω input
2. Power handling > 1 kW, cw or average
3. Linear gain > −6 dB over the field of view
4. Coverage:
   - Toroidal about the platform
   - Minimum elevation 30° (half-power limits for the toroidal coverage)
5. Polarization: Vertical or horizontal (selectable by switching)
6. Installation:
   - 14 in (width)
   - 10 in (height)
   - 39 in (length)
   - Flat metal baseplate under the antenna, 14 × 39 in
7. Operating environment:
   - Airborne platform
   - Maximum temperature: 90°C
8. Storage environment:
   - Depot
   - Maximum temperature: 40°C

solution The coverage requirement calls for omnidirectional coverage and either vertical or horizontal polarization. For vertical polarization, a vertical monopole can be used and fed with the baseplate acting as a ground-plane. For horizontal polarization, the first choice is a horizontal loop. However, the power handling would pose a problem. Also, the horizontal loop mounted above the baseplate would not yield the coverage and the gain would be much lower than −6 dB in the plane of the baseplate. A better solution for the horizontal polarization would be to arrange horizontal dipoles around the edge of the baseplate and sum the dipoles to realize overall coverage. The summing device would cause a reduction in gain.

The installation space imposes limits to the antenna size and, consequently, performance. In terms of wavelengths, the height (10 in) is approximately one-twelfth wavelength at 200 MHz, the width (14 in) is one-tenth wavelength, and the length (39 in) is one-third wavelength. These electrical dimensions would yield antennas with insufficient gain over the field of view (> −6 dB required). For broader bandwidth, the thin dipole elements could be flared. For example, each side of the horizontal dipole could be flared to yield a bow tie shape. Similarly, the thin vertical monopole could be flared to yield a conical structure. Performance would then be improved, but blockage or shadowing would increase, resulting in poorer overall coverage.

A better solution would consist of designing one antenna that radiates both vertical and horizontal polarization without switching. This design would yield lower radiated power for each polarization than a design that used switching. However, it would have fewer blockage effects and better expected overall coverage.

Structurally, the antenna could be built using sheet-metal construction with mechanical stiffeners to handle vibration and shock. Any dielectric materials used in construction should be selected from low loss tangent materials in order to handle a maximum temperature of 90°C plus heating due to power.

Example 4.2 An antenna is to be selected to satisfy the following transmit requirements over the 5.0 to 17.0 GHz frequency range:

1. VSWR ≤ 2/1, referenced to a 50-Ω input
2. Power handling consistent with the radiated power requirement
3. Gain consistent with the radiated power requirement
4. Field of view, 120° × 30° (minimum)
5. Polarization, elliptical with axial ratios not exceeding 6 dB
6. Installation: ogive, one-half section, diameter = 9.0 in
7. Operating environment:
   - Airborne platform
   - Maximum temperature: 95°C
8. Storage environment:
   - Depot
   - Maximum temperature: 40°C
9. Radiated power:
   - Minimum 1 kW at 5 GHz
   - Midband 10 kW
   - Upper band 6 kW

solution The system solution here is to use a multibeam array to cover the field of view of 120°. With modest power (40 W per array element), an array of 8 elements is chosen.

A broad element pattern in the array-plane is required to assure 120° beam coverage. This coincides with a waveguide in which the E-plane beamwidth is very broad. Bandwidth for a standard waveguide is only half an octave so that a ridged waveguide is required.

The VSWR of an open-ended, ridged waveguide is typically 3.5/1, which is a good starting point in achieving a 2/1 VSWR. The preceding considerations lead to an E-plane array of 8 ridged-waveguide horns.

Next, the aperture size in the direction orthogonal to the array must be selected to assure the maximum gain at F_{LOW} without allowing the beamwidth at F_{HIGH} to be less than 30°. For this type of antenna element[1] the beamwidth is given by:

$$\theta = 68 \frac{\lambda}{H}$$

where λ = wavelength = c/f
c = velocity of light
f = frequency

Here, H is the aperture height based upon a beamwidth of 30° defined by one-half power limits.

If the beamwidth at F_{HIGH} is taken to mean one-third power limits, which give the highest average gain over the field of view, then a somewhat larger value of H can be used for improved gain at 5 GHz.

Next, the simplest means for achieving elliptical polarization over the band is to use a design that is external to the array. For this bandwidth, a six-sheet meanderline polarizer (see Fig. 12.1) is required with spacing between sheets at midband of approximately one-quarter wavelength. Taking into account the installation space and wraparound dimensions of the polarizer, about 3 in are left for the linear array. Typically, the array spacing is limited to approximately one-half wavelength at F_{HIGH} for 180° coverage. Over a 120° sector, this spacing can be stretched to 0.55 wavelength.

Using

$$d = .55\lambda = .55\left(\frac{11.8}{18.0}\right) = 0.36 \text{ in}$$

Compute

$$N = \frac{L}{d} = \frac{3.00}{0.36} = 8.3$$

or

$$N = 8.0 \text{ (confirming earlier system value)}$$

[1]The E-field is distributed in the elevation plane with a maximum in the center of the guide tapering off to zero as the cosine of the aperture dimension expressed in electrical degrees.

The operating and storage requirements should be satisfied using ridged-horn antenna elements. They can be made structurally adequate. In addition, the metal structure of the horns is naturally heat sunk to the airframe metal, offering improved reliability and power handling.

Example 4.3 An antenna is to be selected to satisfy the following receive requirements over the 100- to 500-MHz frequency range:

1. VSWR ≤ 2/1, referenced to a 50-Ω input
2. Linear gain > −6 dB over the field of view
3. Coverage:
   - Toroidal about the platform
   - Minimum elevation 30° (half-power limits for the toroidal coverage)
4. Polarization: vertical and horizontal
5. Installation:
   - 14 in (width)
   - 10 in (height)
   - 39 in (length)
   - Flat metal baseplate under the antenna, 14 × 39 in
6. Operating environment:
   - Airborne platform
   - Maximum temperature: 90°C
7. Storage environment:
   - Depot
   - Maximum temperature: 40°C

solution The discussion and analysis given under Example 4.1 are appropriate for the selection process here. In addition, it needs to be ascertained whether continuous full-band performance is required or if tuning is allowed. If tuning is allowed, it complicates the design, but it opens the selection process to alternative choices.

For example, the fan or bow tie antennas do not have to cover the full band. Instead, their impedance (Z) can be found, and, by tuning to resonate the unit, better performance can be achieved. In general, tuned antennas can be made smaller so that better installation results, because the antennas can be positioned further apart and so there is less interaction and shadowing.

Example 4.4 An antenna is to be selected to satisfy the following receive requirements over the 5.0 to 17.0 GHz frequency range:

1. VSWR = 2/1, referenced to a 50-Ω input
2. Gain consistent with the system sensitivity requirement
3. Field of view, 120° × 30° (minimum)
4. Polarization, elliptical with axial ratios not exceeding 6 dB
5. Installation, ½ cylinder, 6 in (diameter) × 12 in (length); bisected cylinder mounted over a metal baseplate

6. Operating environment:
   - Airborne platform
   - Maximum temperature: 95°C
7. Storage environment:
   - Depot
   - Maximum temperature: 40°C

solution The discussion and remarks under Example 4.2 lead to the selection of a ridged-waveguide array. In addition, the space constraints (6 in wide) must be shared with another antenna (approximately 1 in wide). The array and polarizer sized for the transmit (Example 4.2) will just fit, provided wraparound polarizer spacings are reduced and height is trimmed to fit. These dimensional trims of the polarizer and the flat baseplate, even when covered with an absorber, will result in axial ratios in excess of 6 dB at the edges of the field-of-view.[2]

As a final point, the selection of an aperture-type antenna is expected to be least affected by the other antenna. Conversely, the flush aperture could be positioned to least affect the antenna already in place (previous system).

---

[2]System analysis indicates that values greater than 6 dB could be accepted provided 95 percent of the data showed 6 dB or less.

Chapter

5

Design Examples

This chapter provides a few select design examples.

Design Example 5.1

The first example pertains to the design of a coupling network between an electrically short low-frequency antenna and the output stage of the transmitter power amplifier. While not strictly an antenna design, it serves to illustrate the problems confronting the designer in achieving bandwidth and radiation efficiency.

Step 1 is to determine the antenna impedance. For the purpose of this example, it will be taken as $(1.6 - j\ 450)\ \Omega$.[1] The output impedance of the final stage of the power amplifier is 1700 Ω (resistive).

The present problem is to design a coupling circuit between these two impedance levels with the following objective specifications:

1. Transfer bandwidth $\geq$ 10 kHz
2. Transfer peak-to-valley $\leq$ 1 dB
3. Efficiency $\geq$ 20 percent

Solution

Four circuits, as shown in Fig. 5.1, are considered to satisfy this need.

[1]The symbol $(-j\ 450)$ indicates a capacitive reactance.

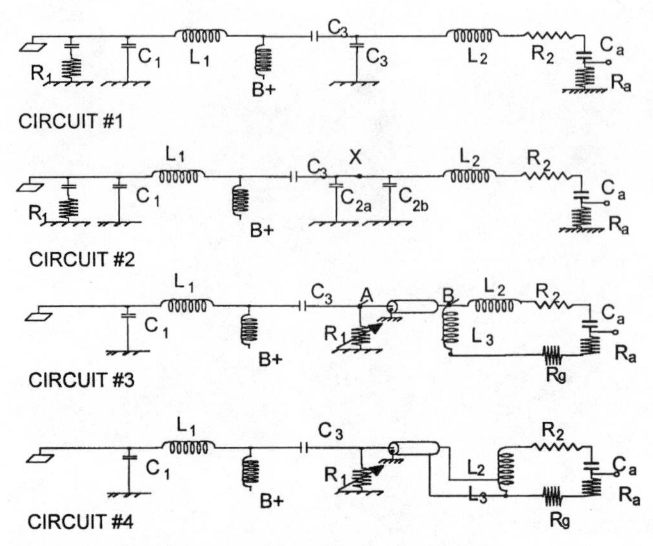

Figure 5.1 Low frequency transmit coupler circuits.

Circuit no. 1 is a double-tuned circuit and may be analyzed on that basis.[2] The design shows good transfer bandwidth and driving point impedance, but poor efficiency. Only 1.7 percent of the input power would be radiated by the 1.6-Ω radiation resistance.

Circuit no. 2 is designed on a power match basis using C2a and C2b to adjust Z, looking backward or forward at point X to be resistive and equal. Acceptable driving-point and transfer characteristics are achieved, but with 5 percent efficiency.

Circuit no. 3 uses the transforming properties of a transmission line. In this figure, $X_{L3} < X_{L2}$ and the transmission line transforms the center-frequency impedance at point B to 50 Ω (resistive) at point A. R_d is used to adjust the transfer bandwidth and peak-to-valley ratio. And since R_d is much greater than 50 Ω, its effect on efficiency is negligible.

Circuit no. 4 uses a single tapped coil in the antenna circuit. Its electrical performance is essentially the same as circuit no. 3. The transfer function is similar to a transitionally coupled, double-tuned circuit.

---

[2]See, for example, Sturley, K. R., *Radio Receiver Design,* Part I, 2nd ed., John Wiley and Sons, New York, 1953; Aiken, C. B., "Two Mesh Tuned Couple Circuit Filters," *Proceedings IRE,* vol. 25, no. 2, February 1937; and *MIT Radiation Laboratory* series, vol. 18, McGraw-Hill, New York, 1948.

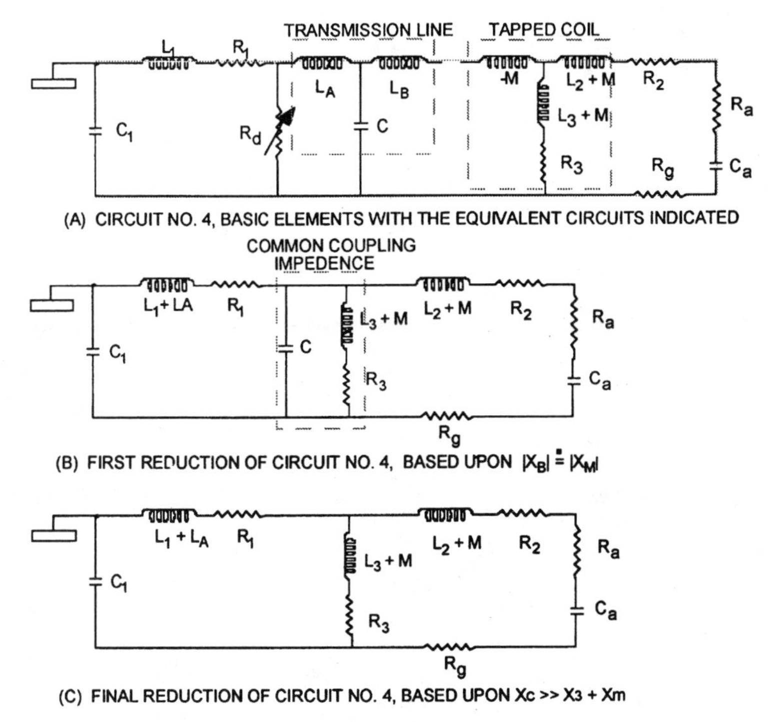

Figure 5.2 Coupler circuit number 4 (reduced).

Redrawing the circuit to that shown in Fig. 5.2 allows the following analysis. If $|X_b| = |X_m|$ and if $X_c \gg (X_3 + X_m)$, the resulting circuit is double tuned and can be treated similarly to circuit no. 1. This configuration appeared to satisfy most of the requirements. The results for the four circuits are given in the table that follows.

Table of Calculated Results

Circuit efficiency[1]		Transfer	Input
Identity	Percent	bandwidth (kHz)[2]	impedance (Ω)[3]
1	1.7	23.0	3900
2	5.0	18.0	2200
3	19.0	18.0	1600
4	22.0	10.0	1700

[1]Fraction of the input power that is radiated by radiation resistance, expressed as a percentage.
[2]Bandwidth for the output circuit defined by the one-half power limits of the radiated power about the center frequency of 300 kHz.
[3]Impedance presented as a load to the power amplifier (output stage).

Design Example 5.2

A requirement exists for a land-based, low-frequency (5 kW) transmitting antenna to be used at 300 kHz and with a height limitation of 150 ft. The objective is to provide the best possible radiated power over at least a 10-kHz bandwidth.

Solution

At 300 kHz, the wavelength equals about 3280 ft, so that the electrical height is only 0.046 wavelength. The design equations needed are

$$R_a = 40\Pi^2 \left(\frac{h}{\lambda}\right)^2 \tag{5.1}$$

where R_a = radiation resistance
h = vertical height
λ = wavelength
$\Pi \cong 3.1416$

$$Z_{o\,avg} = 60\left[\ln\left(\frac{h}{a}\right) - 1\right] \tag{5.2}$$

where $Z_{o\,avg}$ = average characteristic impedance
h = vertical height
a = equivalent radius of the vertical antenna

$$X_a = (Z_{o\,avg})\left[\cot\left(\frac{2\Pi h}{\lambda}\right)\right] \tag{5.3}$$

where X_a = antenna reactance which is capacitive
h = vertical height
λ = wavelength

$$\lambda = \frac{300}{f_{MHZ}} \text{ m} \tag{5.4}$$

First, use Eq. (5.1) to find the radiation resistance,

$$R_a = 395\,(0.046) = 0.84\ \Omega$$

Next, use Eq. (5.2) to find the characteristic impedance. Here the height to diameter of the tower must be selected.

Let $h/d = 15$, so that $h/a = 30$

Then,

$$Z_{o\,\mathrm{avg}} = 60\,[\ln(30) - 1] = 144\ \Omega$$

and using Eq. (5.3),

$$X_a = (144)\cot(360 \times .046) = 471\ \Omega$$

The antenna Q and the bandwidth are,

$$Q = X_a/R_a = 471 = 560$$

$$\text{Bandwidth} = \frac{f}{Q} = \left(\frac{300}{560}\right) = 0.54\ \text{kHz}$$

This may be compared to the required bandwidth and Q (required bandwidth = 10 kHz), so that

$$Q_{\text{required}} = \left(\frac{300}{10}\right) = 30$$

Hence,

$$R_{\text{total}} = \frac{X}{Q_{\text{reqd}}} = \frac{471}{30} = 15.7\ \Omega$$

The antenna-equivalent circuit, including the additional loss, is sketched in Fig. 5.3. Part of the loss resistance occurs due to return currents (currents flowing back through the ground-radial system). Additional loss resistance must be inserted to assure that bandwidth is provided. The radiation efficiency is the fraction of power radiated compared to the input power. To compute this, we can either find the current flowing in R_a and hence I^2R_a or resort to testing a model and measuring the radiated field. The latter method is direct. It is known

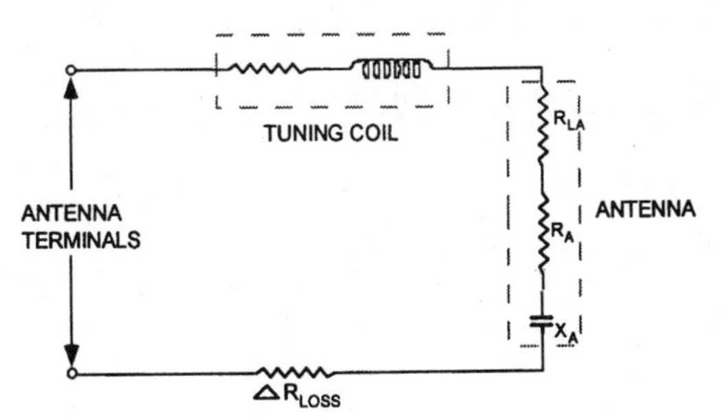

Figure 5.3 Antenna equivalent circuit, losses shown.

that a field intensity of 186 mV/m occurs at one statute mile from a vertical antenna for 1 kW of radiated power. Since $P \alpha E^2$ and E vary inversely with distance, the relationships can be used in a straightforward manner to estimate the efficiency.

Returning to the analysis, the radiation efficiency, neglecting losses in the transformer, is simply

$$n \approx \frac{R_a}{R_{\text{total}}} \times 100 \approx \frac{0.84}{15.7} \times 100 = 5.4\%$$

Consequently, if 5 kW are fed to the antenna, only 5.4 percent of the input power, or 270 W, are radiated. The transformer has losses, probably at least 1 dB, so that the actual radiated power is closer to $270 \times 0.794 = 214$ W.

Design Example 5.3

A requirement exists to design a short array consisting of horn elements to operate over the frequency band from 5.0 to 18.0 GHz. The other requirements follow:

1. Transmission efficiency > 80 percent
2. Power handling per element > 60 W (cw)
3. Size: 3 in wide × 2.5 in high × 4.0 in deep (array without polarization)
4. Element gain consistent with the radiated power requirement
5. Minimum radiated power:

5.0 GHz	1 kW
8.0 GHz	2 kW
12.0 GHz	10 kW
14.0 GHz	10 kW
18.0 GHz	6 kW

6. Field of view: 120° × 30°
7. Polarization: elliptical with the axial ratio not exceeding 7 dB over the field of view
8. Operating environment: −54°C to +95°C
9. Vibration and shock: high-performance, tactical aircraft

Solution

Requirements 1 through 7 pertain to the solution of the design problem. Requirements 8 and 9 pertain to anticipating the effects of environment on the design. Here, the main emphasis will be given to addressing 1 through 7.

Requirements 1 and 2 indicate that no lossy materials should be used in the design. They also indicate that the VSWR for the array with all elements driven needs to be kept under 2.5/1 (i.e., 82 percent transmission efficiency).

The size constraints indicate that an array of E-plane, small horns would serve as a good starting point. To reduce the size and achieve performance over a wide bandwidth, ridges should be used within the horns to lower their cutoff wavelength. For simplicity and a balanced performance, a double-ridged design is selected.

Next, the ridge optimization should be considered. The curves shown in Figs. 5.4 and 5.5 are useful for this purpose. Three parameters are displayed: the ratio of cutoff bandwidths ($\lambda_{c1}/\lambda_{c2}$), the normalized ridge width (s/a), and the ridge separation (d/b). It can be seen that the maximum bandwidth ratio occurs for s/a on the order of 0.3

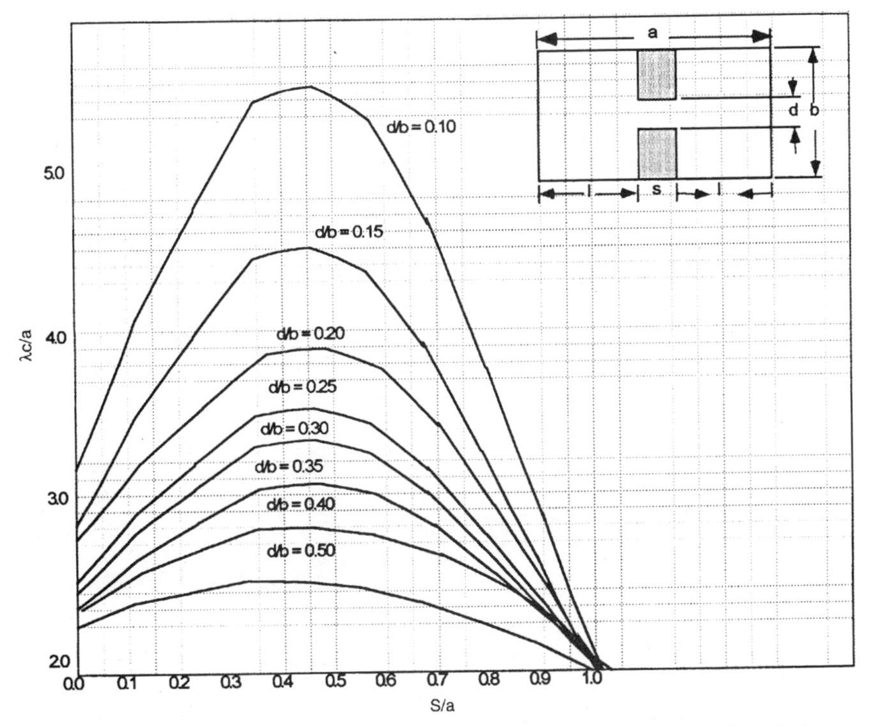

Figure 5.4 Ridge design curves, cutoff wavelength, TE_{10} mode cutoff wavelength, b/a = 0.5. (*Courtesy of PRD Electronics, Inc.*)

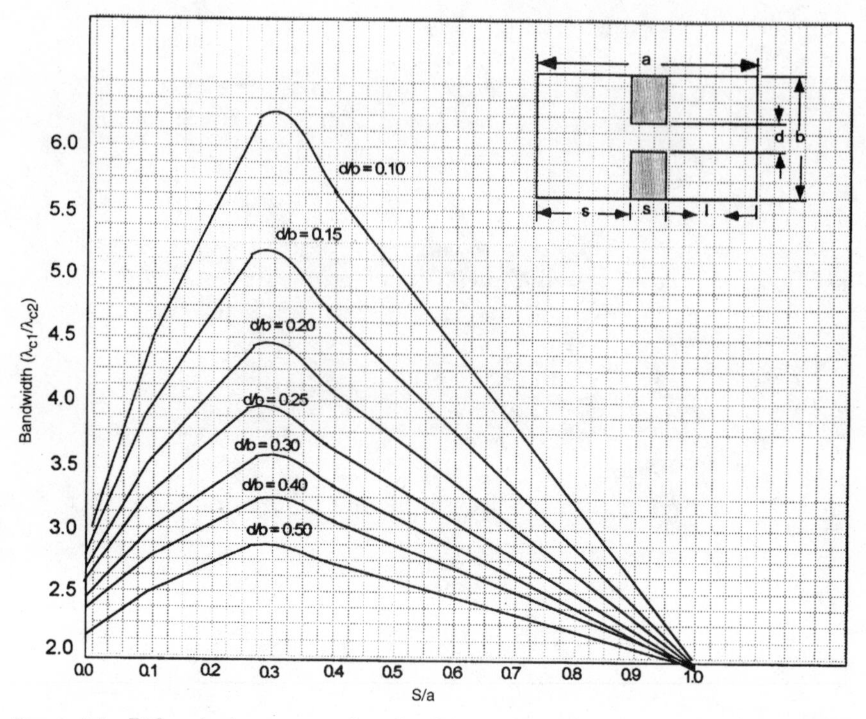

Figure 5.5 Ridge design curves, bandwidth curves ($b/a = 0.5$). (*Courtesy of PRD Electronics, Inc.*)

for all d/b ratios. For the present need, the bandwidth is $18/5 = 3.6$. Thus, a value of d/b on the order of 0.25 will suffice. However, because the bandwidth is likely to shrink between the theoretical value and the realized value when the actual unit is built, a smaller value of d/b should be used.

A minimum value of d/b, based upon safe power handling and avoiding a breakdown voltage problem, would normally be used. Power handling is 60 W per element. Next, derate by a factor of 2. Thus the design voltage between ridges is now based upon 120 W per element in a 50-Ω system, $E^2 = (P)(R) = 120 \times 50 = 6000$ and $E = [(6000)]^{1/2} = 77.5$ V. VSWR effects in the actual unit could reach 3/1, so (conservatively) the peak voltage equals $77.5\ (3)^2 = 700$ V. Referring to the Federal Handbook, the needle-gap breakdown is 300 V per mil separation at sea level. Thus a separation of 2.3 mils is found. For altitude and temperature derating factors, more separation is necessary. A value of 5 is taken for these factors, leading to a minimum allowable spacing of 12 mils. For added insurance, the prototype element should be power-tested under simulated service conditions before releasing the design.

Next, determine the height dimension, which is the H-plane dimension of the horn array element. First, estimate the maximum dimension based upon minimum coverage of 30°. For the E-field distribution (cosine with maximum in the center of the element), the beamwidth is approximately $68(\lambda/H)$. Solving for $H = 68(\lambda/\theta) = 68[(11.8/F_{HIGH})/30] = 1.49$ in. This value of H would result in a 30° half-power beamwidth at 18 GHz.

Before settling on this value of H, check the element gain requirement at the lowest frequency (i.e., 5 GHz).

For one-half wavelength spacing between array elements at near F_{HIGH}, it is found that $\lambda = (11.8/18.0) = 0.715$ in, so that $(\lambda/2) = 0.358$ in.

Thus the number of elements

$$N = \left(\frac{\text{allowable width}}{0.358}\right) = \left(\frac{3.00}{0.358}\right) = 8.4$$

rounding off, $N = 8$ elements.

The radiated power

$$P = (\text{efficiency})\,(\text{element gain})\,(N)^2 \cdot (P_{TWT})$$

Solve for the minimum element gain, assuming 80 percent efficiency and $P_{TWT} = 15$ W, at 5 GHz,

$$\text{Element gain} = \frac{1000}{(15)(8)(0.8)} = 1.30 = 1.1 \text{ dB}$$

Using this element gain, the element dimensions can be found:

$$G_{min} = \frac{4\Pi A n}{\lambda^2}$$

where η = element efficiency of 80%

$$A = \frac{G_{min}\lambda^2}{4\Pi\eta} = \frac{(1.3)(11.8/5)^2}{4\Pi(0.8)} = 0.72 \text{ in}^2$$

but

$$A = H \times (\text{element width})$$

So

$$H = \frac{A}{\text{element width}} = \frac{0.72}{0.358} = 2.0 \text{ in}$$

which exceeds the H dimension (i.e., 1.49 in) based on the minimum coverage at F_{HIGH}.

If the elevation half-power beamwidth is computed for $H = 2$ in,

$$(\text{HPBW}) = 68\left(\frac{\lambda}{H}\right) = 68\left[\frac{(11.8/18)}{2.0}\right] = 22.3°$$

The incompatibility in H is resolved by noting that for the larger dimension higher gain on boresight would result at F_{HIGH}. Thus, at $\pm 15°$ in elevation, the absolute gain would at least equal the gain if the smaller dimension were used. This is illustrated as follows:

First, find the element gain (E.G.) for $H = 1.49$ in.

$$\text{E.G.} = \frac{4\Pi A}{\lambda^2} = \frac{4\Pi(0.358)(1.49)}{(11.8/18)} = 15.6 = 11.9 \text{ dB}$$

At $\pm 15°$ in elevation, the absolute gain $= 11.9 - 3.0 = 8.9$ dB.

For $H = 2.0$ in,

$$\text{E.G.} = 4\Pi(0.358 \times 2.0) = 21.0 = 13.2 \text{ dB}$$

At $\pm 11.15°$ in elevation, the absolute gain $= 13.2 - 3.0 = 10.2$ dB. At $\pm 15°$ in elevation, the gain is

$$\text{E.G.}_{\pm 15°} \approx \left(\frac{22.3}{30.0}\right)^{1/2} \times 10.2 = 8.8 \text{ dB}.$$

Therefore, in realizing the higher gain at 5 GHz by using 2 in for height, essentially no compromise in gain over the field-of-view results at F_{HIGH}. Tentatively, use $H = 2.0$ in for the array height dimension.

We now have the approximate aperture dimensions and the approximate cross-section ridge dimensions. The ridge length should be at least one wavelength at 5 GHz to assure a smooth transition to free-space. Thus, the minimum length (i.e., depth) of the array element equals $\lambda = 11.8/5.0 = 2.36$ in.

Using these dimensions, an array element can be built and evaluated, provided we devise a suitable transition from the coaxial input to

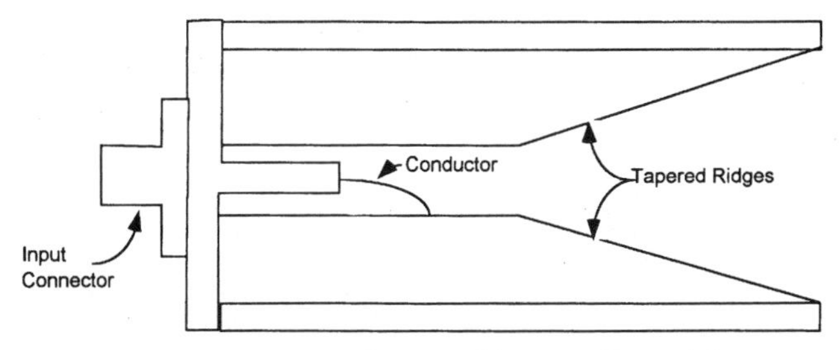

Figure 5.6 Coaxial line to ridge transition, starting point.

the double-ridged waveguide. One type of transition, sketched in Fig. 5.6, showed good performance in a similar application and was selected for use here.

We are now ready to build a breadboard antenna for the following reasons:

1. It provides a model for bench testing and VSWR optimization.
2. It provides a model for chamber tests to verify coverage and gain.

In conducting these tests, the effects of the array on the element need to be known, so at least three elements should be built and testing conducted on all three elements as an array.

Following these tests, a full breadboard array of 8 elements should be built and tested. This allows for determining:

1. Coverage in the array-plane
2. Gain
3. Active VSWR (value for all elements driven simultaneously)

Coverage is found by pattern measurements, one element at a time, with the other elements terminated in 50 Ω. Gain is found by measuring one element at a time with the other elements terminated in 50 Ω. Active VSWR is found by computation, given the passive reflection coefficient (determined one element at a time with the others terminated) and the total coupling from all other elements to each element. Both the passive reflection coefficient and total coupled field are vector quantities and must be combined to determine the active reflection coefficient. The summation at F_{LOW} is illustrated in Fig. 5.7.

A very important point is that the passive reflection may be canceled partially by the total coupled field, yielding a lower value of ac-

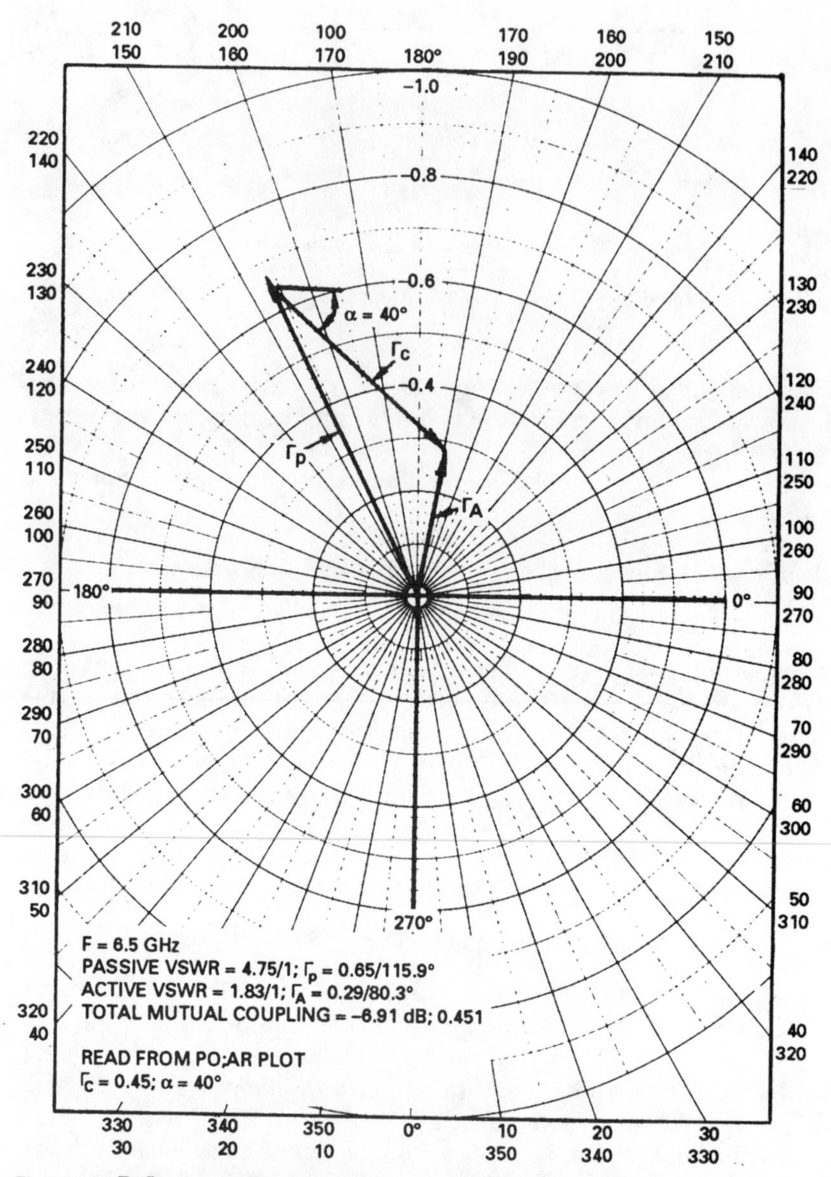

Figure 5.7 Reflection coefficients and coupling at F_{LOW} (+1.5).

Figure 5.8 Eight-element array. (*Courtesy of Raytheon Company*)

tive reflection coefficient with improved VSWR (i.e., transmission efficiency is better than predicted from the passive VSWR).

Figure 5.8 shows the finished array with dimensions conforming to the size requirements. In the finished product, the final height dimension H was 2.25 in, which corrected the 0.1 dB gain deficiency noted earlier.

Chapter

6

Validating the Design

6.1 Introduction

There are two major steps in validating a design. Step 1 involves the analytic process or the paper design. Step 2 involves the modeling process or the breadboard design. A key decision is when to start step 2.

6.2 Paper Design

The first step in the paper design is to gain an understanding of the performance requirements. To accomplish this task, the requirements are first listed. Then a search is made for antenna candidates with performance paralleling the requirements. In general, all of the candidates will satisfy some but not all of the requirements.

Next, the requirements should be prioritized. That is, they should be listed in order of importance and the candidate antennas' capabilities related to this prioritized list. The "fallout" from this activity should lead to two or three primary candidates.

Each candidate should then be considered on the basis of ultimately satisfying the design. The design parameters for each candidate must be examined to assure that none preclude satisfying the requirements. For example, if we are dealing with a waveguide antenna with ridges, is the bandwidth between modes compatible with the requirements or can it be made compatible by making the ridges closer together? And, if so, will the design, operated in its environment, handle the power without breakdown?

Next, the radiating (receiving) properties of the candidate antennas versus the requirements need consideration. Here, the key question is, how well will the design fit the needs? What changes to the basic design will be required?

All of the analyses to this point constitute part of the paper design and provide a rather good understanding of the design parameters versus performance requirements.

We are now ready to formulate some rather simple cause-and-effect equations. For example, if we are dealing with a vertical monopole and a literature search has shown that the ratio of length to diameter affects the input impedance parameters (R and X), then bandwidth parametric curves could be developed from published data and used as a basis for predicting results for the present need. As a second example, if we are dealing with a circularly polarized antenna and it is found that the wrap-tightness of the spiral windings affects the quality of circularly polarized performance, curves displaying circularity (i.e., axial-ratio) versus wrap-tightness can be developed for review. However, with the tighter wrap, the distance to radiation region may increase, so more loss may result. Tradeoffs between these two performance factors can be developed.

Sometimes the literature search is even more useful, yielding design equations for the chosen antenna. In this case, and if a computer is available, the paper design can be optimized. The paper design can be considered complete when first-order estimates of key performance characteristics are available. Even then, the design model is not rigorous, for all of the factors affecting performance may not be contained in the model. To validate the design, a test model should be built and tested.

6.3 Breadboard Model

A breadboard model is essential to prove the design. With this model, the parameters can be "tweaked" or adjusted to achieve the best full-band performance.

6.3.1 Tweaking

Upon receiving the breadboard model and testing, it is found deficient in some areas of performance. Tweaking is in order! Here, an orderly, empirical process is required. Change any design dimension and observe the effects. For example, successively increment the design dimension, observing for each increment how the performance changes. From these observations, the best design value will be found.

Next, conduct similar experiments with each of the other design parameters. The final product represents the "tweaked" design. It will most likely represent some compromises in the design values.

Following the tweaking, it is good practice to build and test a second breadboard with the new design values. In addition to validating the design, this assures that no critical design parameter will be overlooked.

6.3.2 Installation

The breadboard model now needs to be placed in an environment representative of the planned installation and validated. Here, space constraints may force additional "trimming-to-fit." In addition to fitting within the allotted installation space, the antenna must function in the installation environment (i.e., over a metal ground-plane, through a protective radome, under temperature extremes, and the like). All of these criteria will affect antenna performance.

Some solutions may exist to minimize installation effects. For example, when space permits, absorber material can be placed over the ground-plane and around the antenna (inside the radome) to isolate the antenna from the ground-plane. Here, care must be exercised in transmit applications to avoid burning the absorber. Also, for both transmit and receive antennas, care must be taken not to reduce the antenna gain by covering or blocking the antenna aperture.

The proof of any design is the measured performance in the planned (or real) installation!

Chapter

7

Trimming the Design

7.1 Introduction

This chapter describes typical trimming processes, illustrated by various examples.

7.2 Examples

7.2.1 Waveguide element

Figure 7.1 shows the interior of a waveguide array element developed empirically. In the figure, the extent of the ridges, the ridge dimensions, the interior width, and the rounded curvatures were all determined by trial and error to achieve the best overall performance. The only known or fixed dimensions were the outside dimensions of the array element.

The first cut at the interior layout used a standard waveguide and the ridge dimensions were selected to yield the maximum bandwidth between mode cutoff wavelengths. A test model conforming to these dimensions was then built and tested.

Upon examination of the VSWR measurements, it was determined that adjusting the ridge widths might extend the bandwidth. First, the ridge widths were increased and VSWR measured to determine if broader VSWR bandwidth resulted. This action proved unsuccessful. Then, ridge widths were decreased in small steps (roughly 10 percent) and for each width, VSWR versus frequency was recorded. Examination of the results provided a basis for selecting the ridge width.

Next, the effect of the wall behind the probe (region 1) was considered. It was known that the short-circuited waveguide for region 1

Figure 7.1 Layout inside ridged element.

acted as an inductive impedance in parallel with the impedance (taken toward the aperture). Experiments were conducted to minimize the inductive loading, yielding the contours shown in Fig. 7.1.

Next, the transition to the aperture, region 2, was considered. Here, a linear tape was first used. From experience, it was thought that a smooth curve approximating an exponential flare might offer more bandwidth. Thus, the contour was modeled in slightly curved increments and tested at each increment to produce the selected curvature shown in Fig. 7.1.

The extent of the ridges and their length and taper represented the final parameters to be determined. A long, gradual, linear taper was initially selected. Then VSWR tests were conducted to confirm the best bandwidth.

Next, gain for the horn element was measured and optimized. The extent of the ridges was varied to determine the best over-the-band gain characteristic. The best performance was found with the ridges shortened to the length indicated in Fig. 7.1.

Figure 7.2 Vertical monopole and top hat. (*Courtesy of Raytheon Company*)

VSWR for the model was checked and found to be slightly poorer than for the long ridges. Since gain was more important, short ridges were used in the final design.

7.2.2 Vertical monopole

Figure 7.2 shows a photograph of a vertical monopole that was developed empirically.

In Fig. 7.2, the flare angles, the shape of the top hat, and the height of the feed point above the ground-plane were optimized by experimental means.

From published work (Brown and Woodward, 1952), mainly R and X data, it was known that a conical monopole offered wide VSWR bandwidth. A flare angle of 90° appeared best. But, because of the installation space, the 90° flare could not be used for both flare dimensions and still provide the required maximum height. Since maximum height (length) was required to achieve reasonable VSWR and gain at the lowest frequency, it was necessary to find the second flare angle empirically.

Several flare angles near the maximum available angle were tried.

The results showed that 65° was best. Next, the edges defining the 65° angle were modified, first with convex curvature and then with concave curvature. Tests for each curvature indicated that a linear taper would suffice.

The top hat was the next consideration; the maximum size could be rectangular in shape, defined by the flare angles. However, if a rectangle were used, it would result in excessive end-loading of the monopole, possibly causing VSWR problems at the high end of the band. Accordingly, the cap was trimmed to the elliptical shape shown in Fig. 7.2.

The final tweak consisted of checking VSWR as a function of cone-tip height above the ground-plane. It was known from experience and published data that the input impedance changed as a function of height. A height almost flush with the ground plane appeared to yield the best results.

7.2.3 Single notch

Figure 7.3 shows a photograph of a subarray of four notches, with the following dimensions available for optimization:

1. The crossover location of the feed line with respect to the slot ends
2. The end point for the feed line
3. The shape of the notches at the aperture

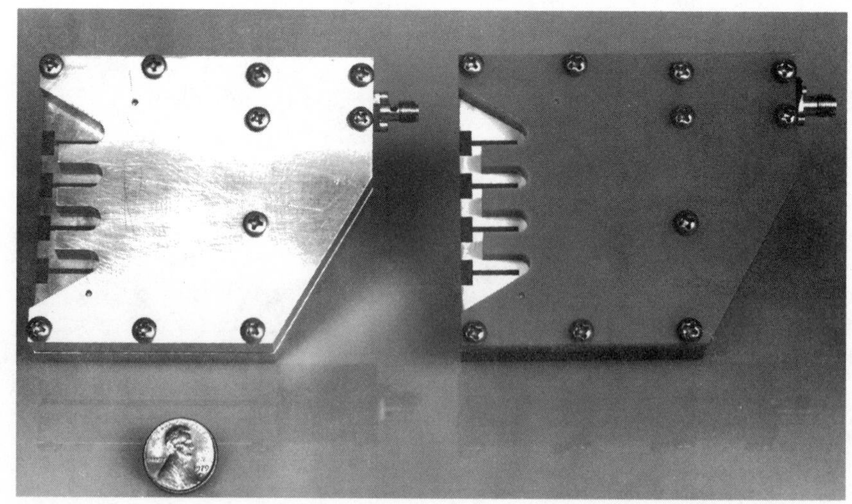

Figure 7.3 Four-notch subarray (in holding fixtures). (*Courtesy of Raytheon Company*)

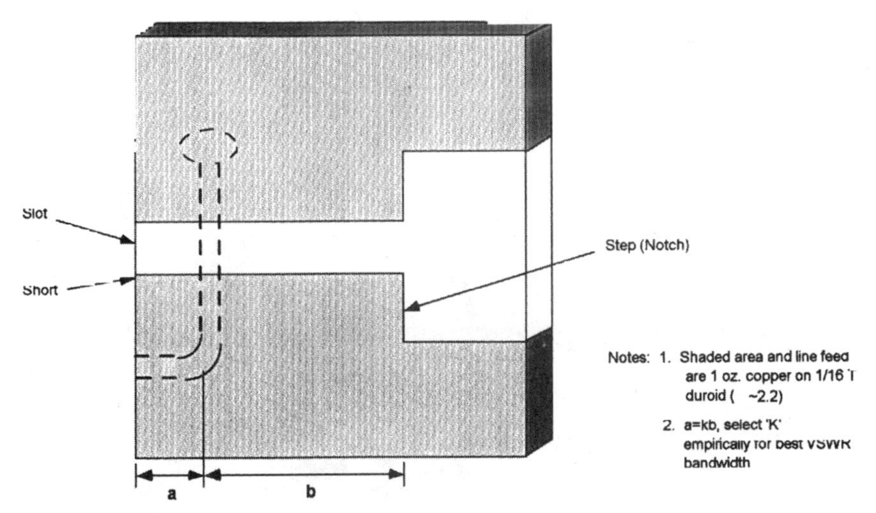

Figure 7.4 Single notch layout.

4. The thickness of and type of material of the substrate, which determine the electrical separation between feed line and slot
5. The width of the feed line

These five design parameters represented too many to tweak arbitrarily.

The material thickness was arbitrarily chosen to avoid moding at high end of the band. A beginning design was built using copper-clad Duroid,[1] illustrated in Fig. 7.4. The input (feed line) is shown with two parallel loading impedances, the inductive impedance for the shorted section of slot and the aperture-loaded section of the slot. In addition, the input feed line shown adds a capacitive impedance in series with the parallel-pair of impedances.

Since the design required 4/1 bandwidth and the notch impedance varies widely over this frequency interval, the optimization steps were small. At the low end of the band, the distance to the short (behind the feed input) was trimmed for best VSWR. Then, slight further trimming was accomplished by adjusting the elliptically shaped coupling disk on the end of the feed line.

For VSWR optimization over the band, both an abrupt step and curvature were tried in the transition to the aperture plane. The

[1]Glass-beaded dielectric manufactured by the Rogers Corporation is similar to Teflon-fiberglass manufactured by 3M.

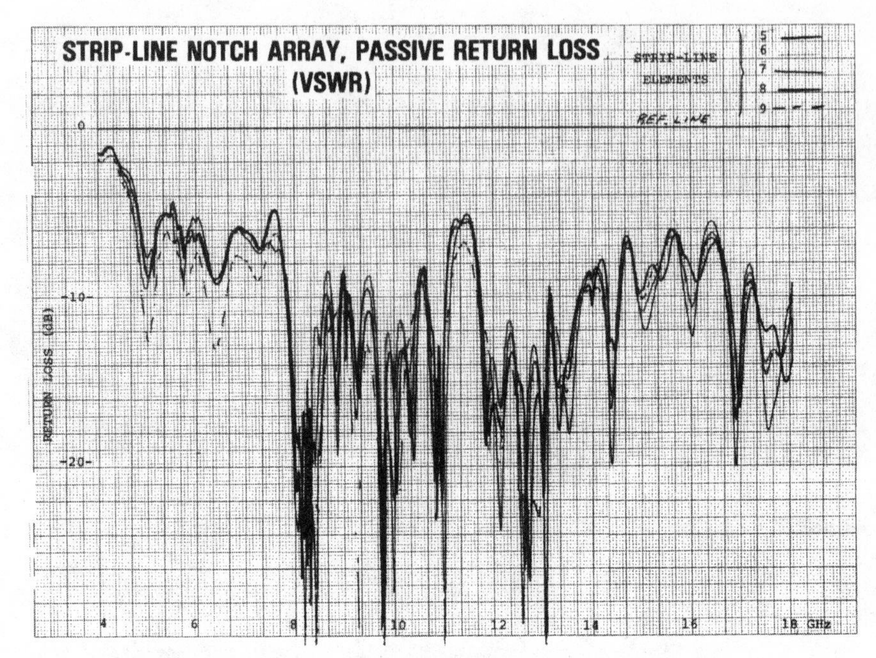

Figure 7.5 Notch array, passive return loss (VSWR). (*Courtesy of Raytheon Company*)

curved or flared notch yielded the best VSWR over the band. However, the stepped notch was selected for use because it required less depth to install. Also, the notch phase center remained closer to the aperture over the band. This is important when an integrated dual polarized element is used to form circular polarization with a 90° hybrid to feed each element. Also, better wide angle coverage would be provided with a stepped notch design. Figure 7.5 shows typical VSWR plots for the stepped notch subarray.

7.3 Concluding Remarks

Examples have been given to illustrate the trimming process. The important point is that a preliminary design is drafted and then refined to yield the final design.

Reference

Brown, G. H., and Woodward, O. M., Jr., "Experimentally Determined Radiation Characteristics of Conical and Triangular Antennas," *RCA Review,* December 1952, pp. 425–452.

Chapter

8

Other Aspects in Validating the Design

Validating the first design requires building a model and extensive testing. Here, the process is illustrated by example.

8.1 Dual Polarized VHF Transmit Antenna

In Chap. 4 a solution was described and parametric limitations, such as the installation volume, were given. These constraints dictate that a test model be built and tested.

The detailed validation process can begin by using a scale model of the full-size model, preferably no smaller than one-tenth of scale. Then, consider reconfirming the results using a one-fifth of scale model. Agreement between results adds confidence in extrapolating the results to a full-scale unit.

Scale model testing is easier because the smaller size and higher frequencies allow the use of a smaller test chamber. The pattern coverage, VSWR, and gain can be determined. To a first order, these results indicate whether a full-size unit scaled from the model is warranted.

Figure 8.1 shows a photograph of a one-tenth of scale model following guidelines given in Chap. 4. The first tests to be conducted are VSWR measurements over the scale model frequency range, extending at least 20 percent beyond the band edges. From these results, three questions can be answered:

- Does the VSWR plot agree with the expected result?
- Is the VSWR under 2/1 with some margin over the band?

Figure 8.1 Dual-polarized VHF antenna, one-tenth of scale. (*Courtesy of Raytheon Company*)

- Does it appear that covering the full band will pose a problem because of the abrupt increases in VSWR near band edges or does the design cover more than the band?

The significance of the first two questions is to determine whether to proceed or look for a new design. The answer to the last question is important! It tells the designer whether to proceed with the evaluation and it shows how difficult it may be to make the VSWR requirement over the band. By checking beyond the band limits, the designer knows what allowances or compromises can be made in building to full scale. For example, in full scale, some dimensions may be reduced further to allow radome clearances. Changes in these dimensions result in shifting the frequency band, say 10 percent. Since the model testing covered more than the required band, the answer is available.

If the scale model is to be used for further tests, a test plan should be prepared to outline the extent of pattern testing and gain. This may take the form of a rather detailed plan if the tests are to be conducted without the designer present or it can be a rather short plan if the tests are conducted by the design engineer. The important point is that the number of patterns, gain measurements, and gain-point locations on

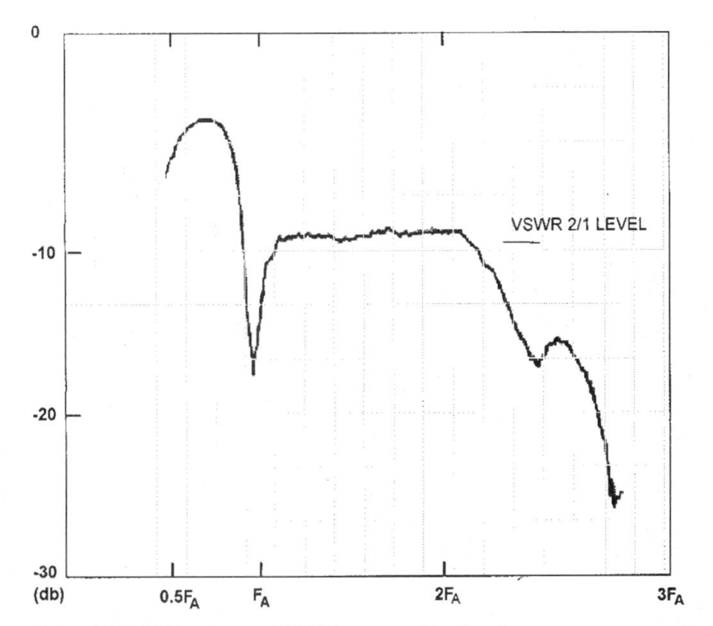

Figure 8.2 VHF antenna, VSWR, one-tenth of scale.

the patterns all need to be indicated. A simple matrix of the plan can prove useful during the testing to make sure nothing is missed.

Figure 8.2 shows a VSWR plot for the model shown in Fig. 8.1. In this figure, the scale model frequency band is shown and the objective VSWR limit of 2/1 is indicated. From this plot, it can be seen that holding the VSWR under 2/1 will prove difficult because some of the in-band values are close to or exceed the limit. Also, the VSWR shows a significant increase as the frequency approaches the lower limit, indicating that scaling to full size may be a problem when allowances for installation clearance and tolerances are imposed.

Now, consider the pattern and gain measurements that need to be defined to ensure that the design satisfies the design objective. Figure 8.3 shows the antenna in the test coordinates dimension. Pattern measurements are taken in the principal planes for the antenna under test, here defined as the *X-Y* and *X-Z* planes.

For the first pattern, the sampling can be as coarse as 10 patterns over the band in each plane. Examination of these plots should reveal whether to proceed with more measurements, defining closer increments, or whether to refine the design (change the dimensions slightly) and try again. The decision process to proceed is based upon whether the patterns at least cover the field-of-view without any

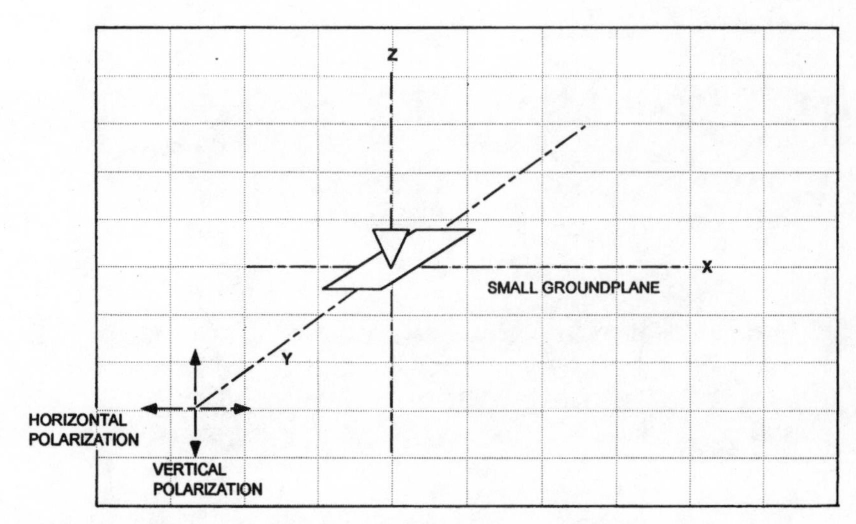

Figure 8.3 VHF antenna, test coordinates for patterns and gain.

TABLE 8.1 Coverage Assessment

Frequency: ____________ Source Polarization: ____________

	Azimuth angle in degrees								
	−60	−45	−30	−15	0	+15	+30	+45	+60
Elevation angle (degrees)									
+15									
0									
−15									

1. All pattern levels to be entered into the table are in dB normalized to the level at 0, 0° (e.g., antenna boresight).
2. Testing is conducted by rotating the antenna-under-test about the *Z*-axis.
3. All angles are oriented with respect to antenna boresight (0,0°, e.g., the *Y*-axis).

dropouts. If the pattern coverage is adequate, then the gain needs to be found on one point of the reference set of patterns over the band, including the frequency band edges. The results of the pattern measurements and gain can be assembled into tables, as shown in Tables 8.1 and 8.2. Table 8.1 shows the coverage assessment and Table 8.2 shows the gain assessment.

Figure 8.4 shows typical patterns for this model. It shows good omni coverage for vertical polarization. The coverage for horizontal

TABLE 8.2 Gain Assessment

Frequency:________ Source Polarization:________

	Azimuth angle in degrees								
	−60	−45	−30	−15	0	+15	+30	+45	+60
Elevation angle (degrees)									
+15									
0									
−15									

1. All gain-recorded-levels are in dB with respect to a known gain standard.
2. Testing is conducted by positioning the antenna to a set of coordinates and then sweeping across the frequency band and recording the level with respect to the standard (i.e., the reference level).
3. All angles are with respect to antenna boresight (0,0°, e.g., the Y-axis).
4. Absolute gains are then found and entered into the table to assess compliance.

polarization is not adequate, for it exhibits four significant areas of poor response. This model warrants no further tests and evaluations.

If above results had shown acceptable coverage, then a second model, using one-fifth of scale for convenience, could be configured and tested. Testing and evaluation similar to the first model's tests would then be performed and related to the one-tenth of scale tests. If the results correlated within 10 to 15 percent, then a full-scale model would be built for test.

The full-scale model for the VHF unit and installation is large, cumbersome, and expensive to fully test. As a minimum, VSWR and gain data should be taken. These results can be compared to the scale model results. If they agree within 10 to 15 percent and satisfy the requirements, then the design is probably adequate. However, for added assurance or upon the customer's request, some full-scale pattern testing may be conducted. Again, these results can be compared to the scale model results for confirmation of the design.

The remaining full-scale parameter to be tested concerns power handling in the operation environment. This test is rather expensive to conduct because it requires simulation of the environment and a power source. In configuring the full-scale model, care was exercised in selecting low-loss dielectrics and in the selection of the antenna feed transmission line. Based upon published data, the safe power handling of the input line can be found and derated by a factor of 2 to 3 for expected temperature and altitude effects. Also, the spacing and support structure at the feed point must be set to ensure that no

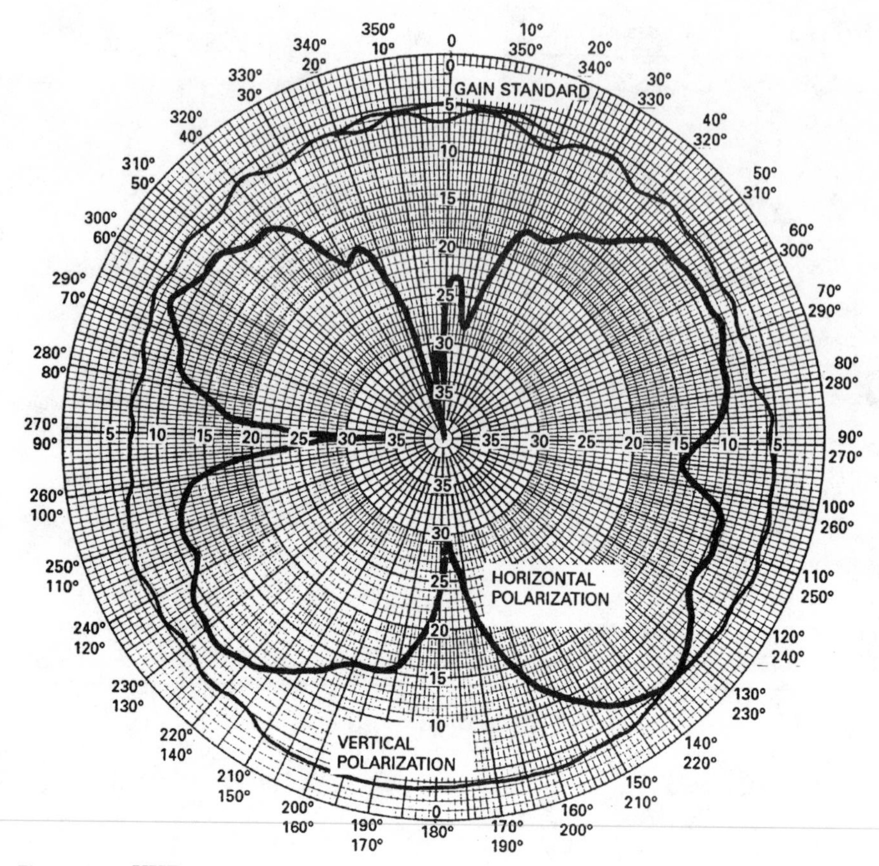

Figure 8.4 VHF antenna, typical dual-polarized pattern. (*Courtesy of Raytheon Company*)

breakdown occurs due to peak voltages and worst-case VSWRs. Here, published data and possibly 60-cycle peak voltage testing may be used to confirm the design. Appendix A shows what is typically involved where power testing is a requirement.

8.2 Microwave Array (5 to 18 GHz)

In Chap. 5, the basic elements in the paper design were described. Here, the validation process will be described. The validation process begins with constructing a test model for the following reasons:

- It provides a model for bench testing and VSWR optimization.

Figure 8.5 Eight-element microwave array. (*Courtesy of Raytheon Company*)

- It provides a model for pattern and gain tests.
- It provides a model for active VSWR measurement (all array elements simultaneously driven).
- It allows assessment of interactions and shadowing effects particularly when more than one antenna coexist in close proximity in the same installation.
- It allows verification of power handling under simulated operating conditions.

Figure 8.5 shows the final form of the eight-element array, which is identical to the breadboard array with respect to the interior construction and dimensions.

Figure 8.6 shows representative VSWR plots for the array elements taken in the passive mode. That is, each array element is tested with all other elements loaded with 50-Ω terminations. These plots show the expected behavior for ridge-loaded horns: rather poor VSWR at the low end of the band with improved VSWR at the middle and upper band. These plots would seem to be of concern because of the poor VSWR over the lower part of the frequency band. However, to keep on schedule, the other performance characteristics were examined before undertaking a new design.

The next task undertaken is to measure the active VSWR. There are two ways to make this measurement: (1) measure the VSWR of each element with all other elements driven simultaneously or (2) measure the complex coupling and passive reflections and then calculate the active reflection coefficients and VSWR.

In the first arrangement, identical dual-directional couplers are

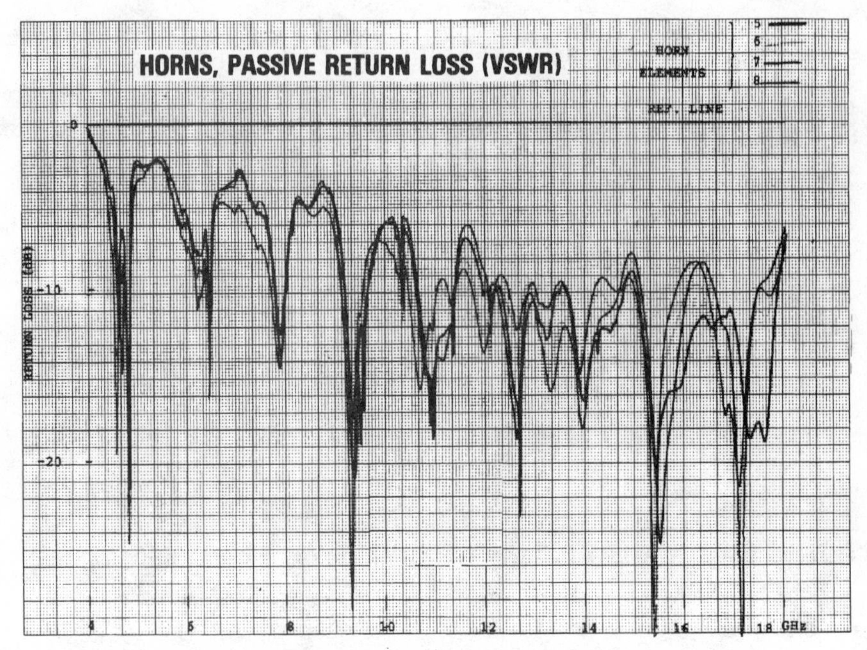

Figure 8.6 Array element, passive VSWR. (*Courtesy of Raytheon Company*)

placed ahead of each array element and all elements are simultaneously driven as shown in Fig. 8.7. Then, by measuring the ratio of the forward power to the reflected power, the VSWR can be found.

In the second arrangement, a network analyzer, capable of measur-

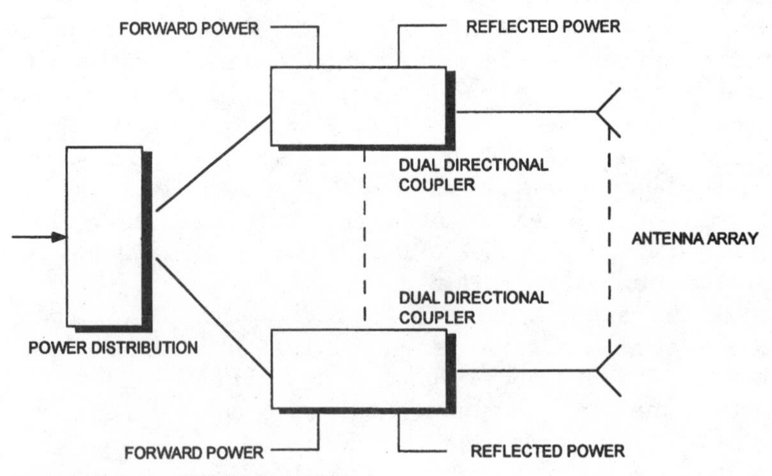

Figure 8.7 Active VSWR, test setup.

ing the complex phase of the reflection coefficient and the complex phase of the coupled energies, is required, as detailed in Appendix B.

When the active VSWRs were found by using the network analyzer, they showed remarkably good VSWR over the band on boresight, pointing to good transmission efficiency on the order of 75 percent. For a pair of driven elements, low active VSWR yields the best element gain (Ludwig, 1976).

The active VSWRs were also computed for ±30° and ±60° from boresight to assess the useful field-of-view for the array. Here, any significantly high VSWRs (greater than 6/1) could lead to holes in the pattern coverage. These results showed that only at ±60° (and then rarely) 6/1 VSWRs were found. No holes in the pattern coverage were expected based upon this analysis.

Figures 8.8 through 8.10, selected from a host of patterns, are typ-

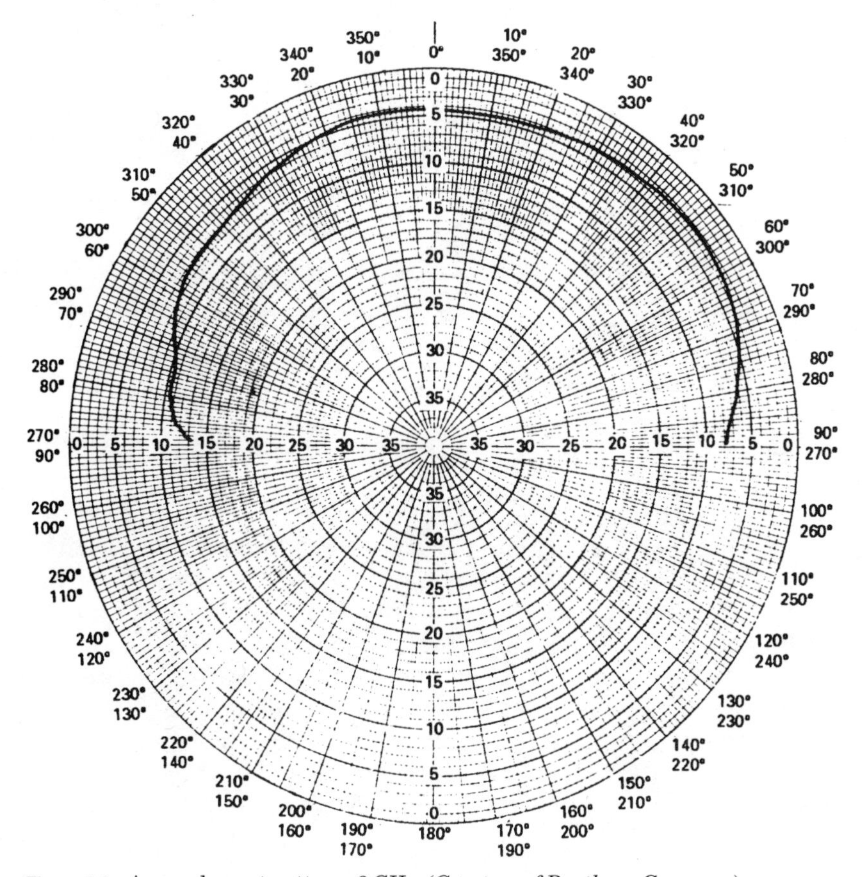

Figure 8.8 Array element pattern, 6 GHz. (*Courtesy of Raytheon Company*)

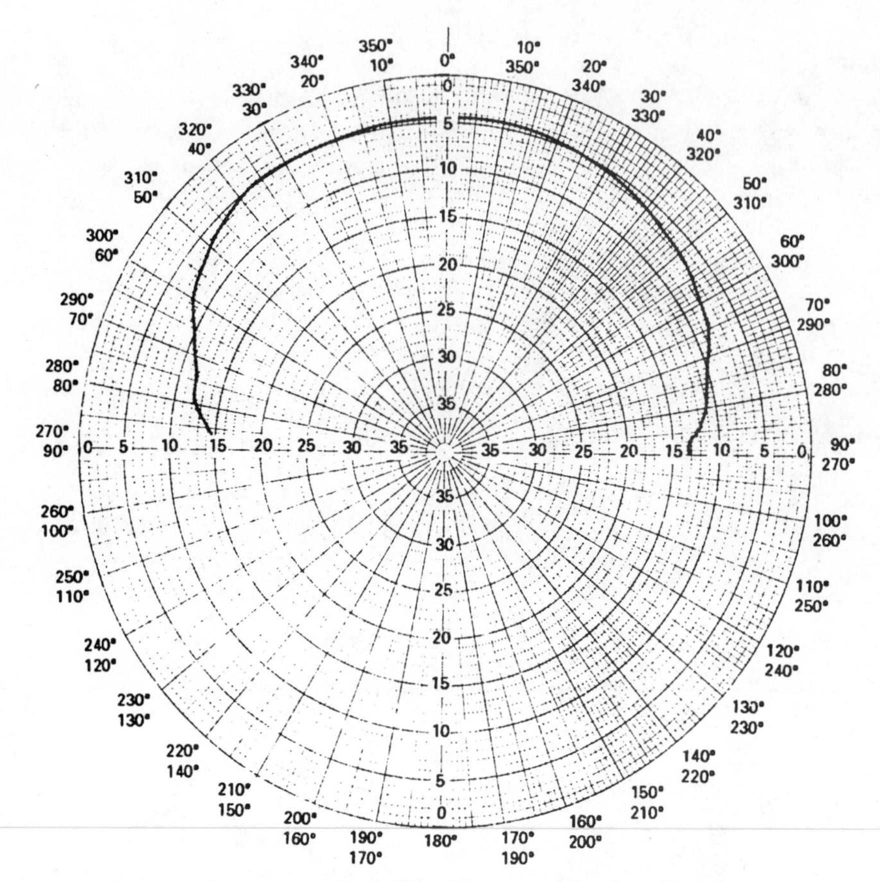

Figure 8.9 Array element pattern, 12 GHz. (*Courtesy of Raytheon Company*)

ical element patterns for the array at low, middle, and upper frequencies. No holes in coverage over ±60° from boresight were observed.

Figure 8.11 shows typical element gain on boresight. When all the preceding results were compared to the requirements, they indicated satisfactory performance.

A final series of tests was then conducted to determine the power handling the array element under simulated environmental conditions to assure that the input connector, transition, and closely spaced ridges would handle the power with some safety margin.

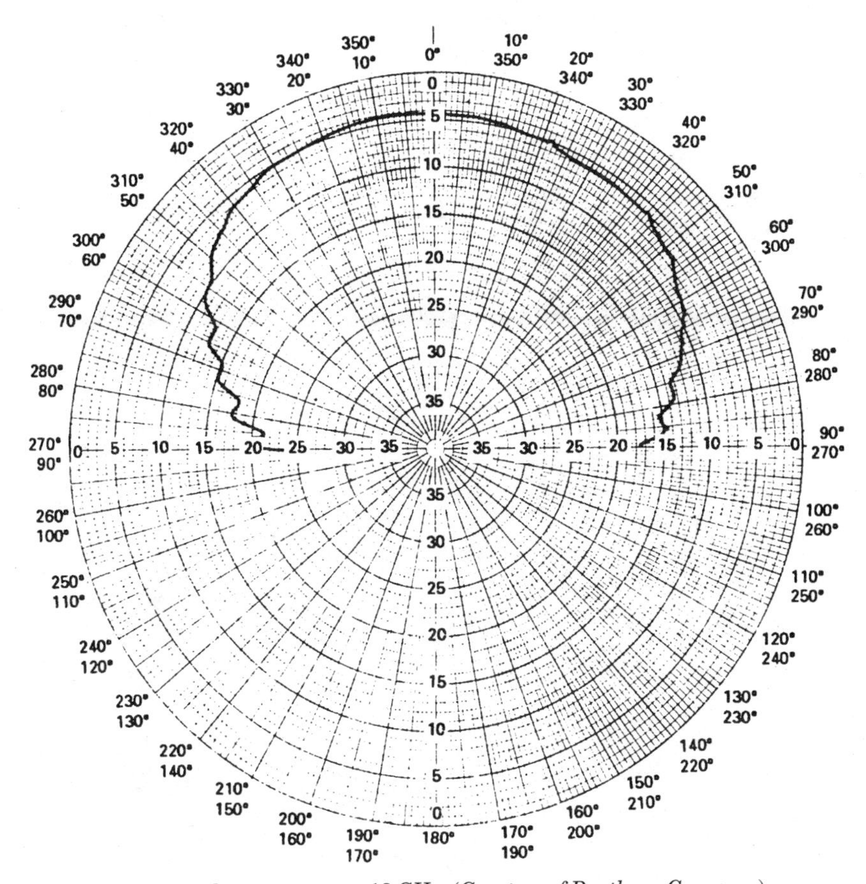

Figure 8.10 Array element pattern, 18 GHz. (*Courtesy of Raytheon Company*)

These tests revealed that at least a 20 percent safety factor existed for the design.

8.3 Concluding Remarks

The ultimate objective of the validation process is to determine whether the design will meet a set of predetermined requirements or specifications with some margin for performance in production. In order to provide a guide for similar evaluations, the validation steps were detailed for both design examples.

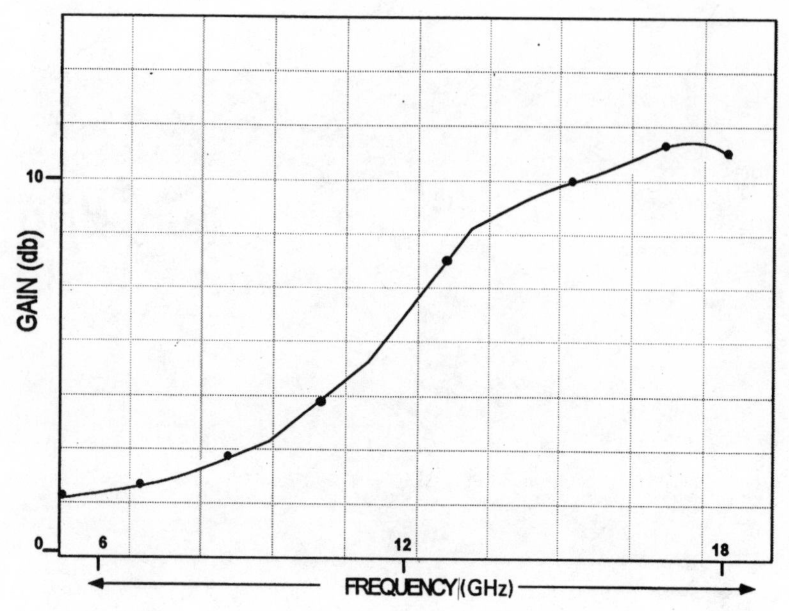

Figure 8.11 Microwave array, average element gain. (*Courtesy of Raytheon Company*)

Reference

Ludwig, Arthur C., "Mutual Coupling, Gain, and Directivity of an Array of Two Identical Antennas," *IEEE Transactions,* AP-24: 837–841, 1976.

Chapter

9

Avoiding Design Pitfalls

In this chapter, we emphasize the importance in avoiding design pitfalls, including the following:

- Configuring a design with tight mechanical tolerances
- Releasing a design that just meets the design requirements

9.1 Mechanical Tolerances

One of the purposes of a detailed validation process is to discover and avoid, if at all possible, close tolerances in the design. For example, when designing the horn array element (Fig. 9.1), it was necessary to determine the sensitivity in performance for various inside tolerances. The structure consisted of a ridge-loaded waveguide with a curved back wall. Since no published data covering this configuration could be found, the tolerance study was done empirically.

The array element was first set up for swept plots of passive VSWR versus frequency. Data were then taken for various lengths of ridge taper, beginning with the taper ending at the aperture and successively shortened. This effort showed that the present placement of ridge-length/taper for changes in the length dimension of ±10 percent was hardly noticeable. Similarly, for the selected ridge length, the performance was nearly insensitive to ridge width, so that ±5 percent was allowable. During design, the separation between the top and bottom ridges needs to be maintained to ensure that no power-handling problems would occur; however, a 5 percent increase in spacing

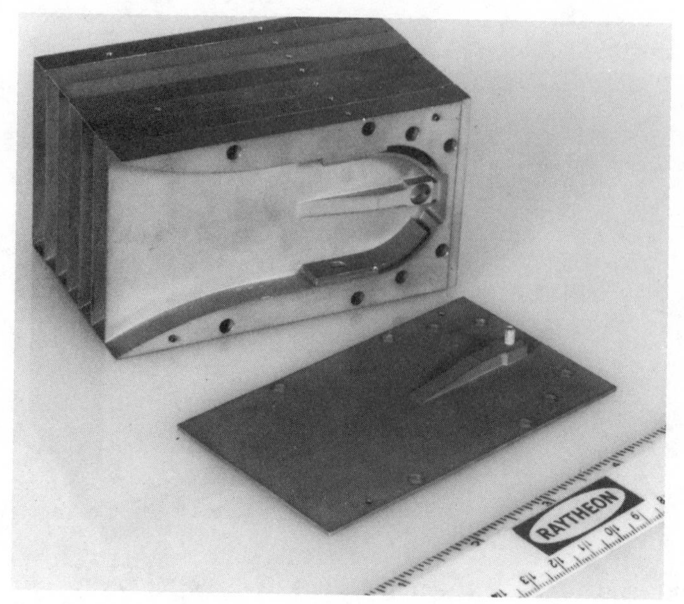

Figure 9.1 Horn element, inside layout. (*Courtesy of Raytheon Company*)

did not seem to affect performance. For the ridge-loaded waveguide, all three of these variables affected the lower frequency cutoff. Here, they did not seem to affect the usefulness of the design down to 5 GHz, the lower band limit. Tests were then run in successive steps to check the back wall curvature and the hole and pin size effects. It was found that the design was rather insensitive to the hole and pin size, but that the curvature was more critical (estimated at ±3 percent). Here, the curvature was modified by adding adhesive-backed copper foil along the back side walls to change the curvature. Finally, adhesive-backed copper foil was added in successive layers and tested to determine the criticality of the waveguide width. Also, the inside width was increased by 20 percent. These results confirmed that the width was not critical (±5 percent).

When the basic unit configuration was gain-tested, it was found that a very narrow-frequency dropout (as shown in Fig. 9.2) occurred near 13 GHz. This result was not expected from the VSWR plots. Next, the wider width unit was checked and the gain dropout shifted down to 11.3 GHz. Various tests were then conducted without success to remove the dropout. It was finally deduced, by lossy loading the inside side walls, that currents on the side walls were responsible for the dropout.

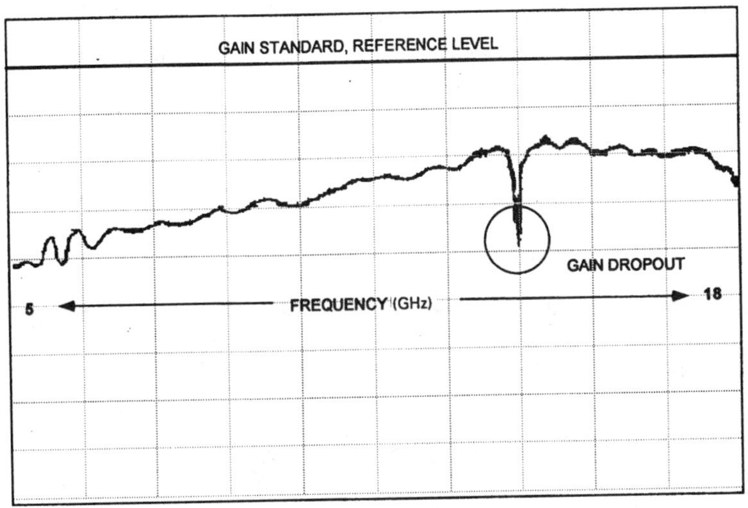

Figure 9.2 Swept gain showing a gain dropout. (*Courtesy of Raytheon Company*)

Adding three-fourths wavelength traps on each side wall cleared the gain dropout problem. It was then determined that the lengths of these traps could vary by ±5 percent without losing their effectiveness.

Overall, it appeared that the design was insensitive to small dimensional changes on the order of ±5 percent. Later, if the elements were to be cast rather than machined, the casting tolerances would probably be acceptable, resulting in a more cost-effective design.

9.2 Marginal Performance

When a breadboard or scale model show marginally acceptable performance, release of the design poses a problem.

For example, in going from the scale model to the full size, there are other factors that, when introduced, can affect performance. Typically, the scale model is evaluated without consideration of allowances for radome removal and sway clearance between the units. Also, additional supporting structure(s), not present in the scale model, may need to be added. The effect of adding clearances can shrink the full size by 5 to 10 percent or more in some cases. Thus, if the VSWR or gain requirement was just met at the lower frequency, it may not be met with the slightly reduced-size unit. For this reason, the performance near the low end of the scale model test band needs to be observed to see whether an adequate margin will exist for scaling the full-size unit.

The other area that should be addressed concerns the addition of support structures to the full-size unit that did not exist in the scale model. Here, the addition of low-loss dielectric supports may affect the coverage; the best way to avoid this type of problem is to coordinate the mechanical and electrical designs during the scale model test design and to include support-blockages in the final tests.

9.3 Concluding Remarks

The ultimate objective of the tolerance study and performance analysis is to uncover and circumvent potential problem areas which could occur after releasing the design for production. These techniques were illustrated using specific designs. However, the principles behind these techniques can be used as a guide for avoiding problems in other similar designs.

Chapter

10

First Model Tests

This chapter describes how to set up a test plan matrix, which is used to check the first model configured to the design to be released for prototype development.

10.1 Scope of Testing

The written requirements need to be translated into a working form that will provide sufficient data to measure the following:

- In-band performance versus the requirements
- Margin of performance versus the requirements
- Extensions that may exist beyond the requirements

To obtain the first objective, the in-band performance, a matrix can be set up to identify the necessary data to be acquired.

The second objective requires a finer detailing of the matrix to ensure that nothing important is missed.

The third objective, checking beyond the band limits, gives insight into the true bandwidth of the design.

10.2 Test Methods

Basically, antenna range testing can be performed by making principle-plane cuts corresponding to X-Y and X-Z cuts with the antenna-under-test at the origin, aligned with the X-axis. The results from these tests provide coverage information in two planes.

The preferred antenna test range is one that allows not only principle-plane cuts, but conical cuts at various elevation planes parallel to the X-Y plane.

The range should also be capable of broadband gain measurements. Appendix C describes how to calibrate your own gain standards.

10.3 Matrix Definition

For the purpose of defining a matrix, it is assumed here that the antenna test range is capable of both principle-plane and conical cuts.

Now consider, for example, Design Example no. 5.3. The coverage, looking forward from the array, is 120° in the array plane and 30° in the elevation plane. Thus, a "space rectangle" of 120° × 30° represents the coverage requirement. A 100 percent test for compliance would require determination at all points within the rectangle. By measuring patterns in the elevation principle-plane (i.e., normal to the array), it is first determined whether the pattern function is smooth and monotonic over the required elevation sector. Next, three conical cuts 0° and ±15° in elevation should suffice for completing the space rectangle of coverage.

The next parameter that needs to be defined is the number of frequencies for pattern tests. Here, swept gain measurements taken on-axis and at ±60° from boresight in the array plane are useful. If the plots show small (less than 3 dB or 4 dB) variations of over 10 percent changes in frequency, then patterns spaced at equal increments including band limits of 10 or 20 percent of the band should suffice. This is probably acceptable because swept gain data will be taken over the band for various points on the space rectangle including the corners.

10.4 Matrix

Figure 10.1 shows a head-on picture of the antenna under test and identifies the space rectangle. Table 10.1 shows the test matrix to define the scope of tests for the first model evaluation.

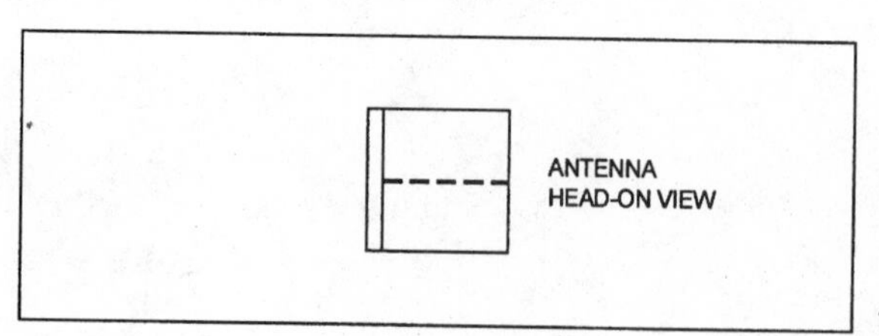

Figure 10.1 Horn element under test, head-on view.

TABLE 10.1 Test Matrix for Patterns (or Gain)

Source polarization: ______________________________

Conic angle: ____________ (referenced to the X-Y plane at 0°)

Limits of angular sweep ± about Z-axis ____________ (referenced to the Y-axis at 0°)

Pointing coordinates: ____________ (referenced to antenna boresight 0,0°)

Gain standards:

Name or type: ____________ Frequency range: ____________

Name or type: ____________ Frequency range: ____________

Swept frequency limits: ____________ to ____________

1. Select only those parameters that apply according to the test or consolidated tests.
2. Under standards and frequency limits note whether the values are kHz, MHz, or GHz.

10.5 Concluding Remarks

The approach for setting up a test matrix was described and a matrix useful for first model testing was provided. This methodology is readily extendable to testing other antenna configurations.

Chapter 11

Analyzing Test Results

Once a bank of data is acquired, it must be studied to analyze it for compliance to requirements and to determine if a design margin exists.

The task of determining compliance is straightforward: the measured data are compared to the requirements.

The task of determining if a design margin exists, and how much, is not straightforward. It requires extrapolation from the model tests to the final configuration and, in some instances, validation with the final model, full installation.

11.1 Compliance Analysis

The matrix tables given in Chaps. 8 and 10 provided a guide to determine compliance. All the requirements are entered into a matrix, and then the measured data are entered into the same matrix. Both are then compared for compliance.

The following items are representative of the imposed requirements:

- VSWR
- Power handling
- Gain
- Coverage
- Polarization purity

The VSWR and power-handling analysis are simple to verify. Either the unit passes or fails the requirement.

TABLE 11.1 Matrix for Gain Analysis

Frequency______				Polarization______					
	Azimuth angle in degrees with respect to boresight (0,0 degrees)								
	−60	−45	−30	−15	0	+15	+30	+45	+60
Elevation angle (degrees)									
+30									
+15									
0									
−15									
−30									

1. The + and − signs are used to indicate position with respect to antenna boresight (i.e., 0,0°).
2. Enter all gain values in the correct coordinate locations.
3. Compare gain values to specification values for compliance.
4. All measured values must equal or exceed the specification to pass.
5. If any measured values are suspect, retest may be warranted.
6. Recheck for specification compliance.

The gain and coverage analyses can be performed using a matrix to assemble the data versus the requirements, as depicted in Table 11.1 for gain analysis. A similar table can be developed for coverage analysis.

Polarization purity requires two tests per pattern. First, the unit is tested for the principal polarization. Next, the source polarization is rotated 90° to determine the cross-polarized response, holding all signal conditions constant per pattern. There is one exception and that occurs when the crossed-signal response falls below normal recording levels. A linear amplifier may be inserted ahead of detection to boost the level for recording. For example, suppose 20 dB is required to bring the pattern up for recording and that the observed level is 15 dB below the principal response. Then the true cross-polarized response is −35 dB (quite good). A matrix can be used to assess if the crossed-polarization response (i.e., polarization purity) is compliant.

11.2 Design Margin Analysis

In the earlier text, the need for acquiring sufficient data to permit margin analysis was discussed. There is never enough data for this task. Taking data beyond band limits and over-stressing (when power testing) were emphasized. Both of these approaches are useful and yet they may not be sufficient.

Consider the VSWR test. If the design is for a transmitting antenna, then the application of power will result in thermal effects that cannot be duplicated by simply heating the antenna in an oven. Had the power testing been conducted in a swept mode and the VSWR monitored, the answer would be available. If these data are not available, then a written analysis may be required to verify minimum thermal effects.

As a second VSWR example, consider the microwave array. If an external polarizer is to be used and it is positioned close to the face of the array because of the installation, a shift in the VSWR profile may occur. Here, data taken with and without the polarizer in place provide information for shift analysis.

Now, consider pattern coverage. Support structures, modeled during development, allow assessment of the design margin in part. However, there are two additional points to consider. First, modeling is frequently done under free-space conditions. In reality, there may be other antennas in close proximity (see Fig. 11.1). During development, some ray-tracing analysis may be performed to assess blockage, but a full installation validation test will be required.

Figure 11.1 Horn array with blockage. (*Courtesy of Raytheon Company*)

The second effect concerns the impact of the radome and the introduced uncertainties that can only be resolved in final model testing of the fully operational installation. Here, limited data may need to be taken to assess the radome effect, for if squint occurs due to the radome, then some loss in pattern coverage could result, thus reducing the design margin.

Finally, consider the gain determination. Two items can work to reduce the design margin, the loss due to an externally added polarizer and the loss due to the radome. The loss of a well-designed polarizer is only a few tenths of a decibel. On the other hand, the radome loss may be greater, particularly if it was not designed for use with the antenna. The effects upon gain will require full installation tests.

11.3 Concluding Remarks

The assessments of pass or fail were described and the process was shown to be straightforward. On the other hand, the assessments of design margins were shown to be rather complicated and, in some instances, warranted full-scale tests in the actual installation.

Chapter

12

Forming Circular Polarization

There are two known methods for generating circular polarization using the microwave array as an antenna. The structure can be modified to include a second polarization orthogonal to the array and then arranging for the principal and added polarizations to be 90° apart in time. A simpler method is to leave the array unchanged and to add an external polarizer in front of the array.

Two possible polarizer designs were considered; a Lerner polarizer (Lerner, 1965) and a Meanderline polarizer (Hacking et al., 1969). The Meanderline design was selected for implementation because of its greater bandwidth.

12.1 Meanderline Polarizer

The Meanderline polarizer was invented at Stanford Research Institute (SRI). Once its properties became known, it found wide application.

The basic design consists of imprinting a meanderline on thin dielectric sheets and orienting the layout 45° with respect to the principal polarization. For multioctave bandwidths, six successive sheets are required, spaced approximately one-quarter wavelength apart at midband, as illustrated in Appendix D. The resulting performance shows two points of excellent axial ratios spaced approximately an octave apart. Reasonably good axial ratios (under 5 dB) are maintained over the full 5 to 18 GHz band on the array boresight. Over the full field of view of 120° × 30°, the axial ratios are typically under 6 dB; however, a few values up to 8 dB can be observed.

Figure 12.1 shows a sketch of the transmit polarizer. Observe that the meanderline sheets are mounted on honeycomb and that air

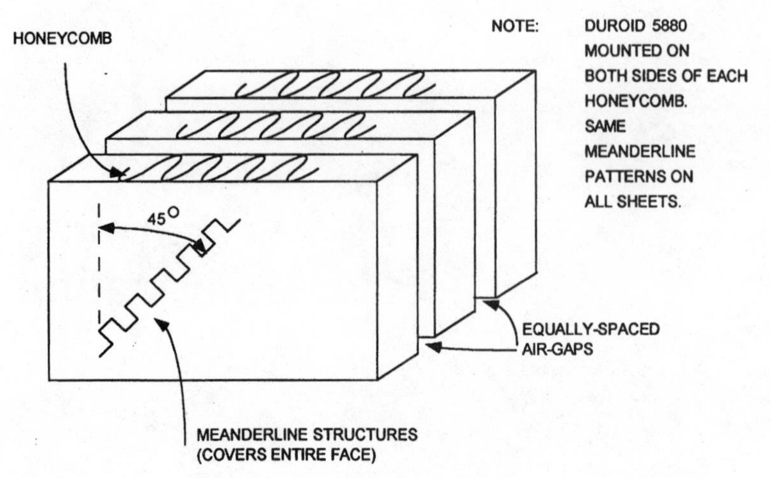

Figure 12.1 Transmit polarizer, six sheets (wraparound sections not shown).

spaces for circulation are provided. Ideally, the polarizer structure would be positioned a sufficient distance from the array face to eliminate interactions that modify the VSWR and axial ratio performance. In the present design, space permitted only a small separation from the array face. And, furthermore, in the wraparound regions, the separation of successive layers of meanderline sheets were reduced to approximately one-eighth wavelength. Notwithstanding these conditions, the design performed to the levels noted earlier, and it complied with the design requirements.

Successful power testing was conducted with the full array energized. Also, single element power tests were run beyond the requirements to measure the design safety margin.

12.2 Concluding Remarks

A brief discussion of the meanderline polarizer design was given along with the achieved performance. Even though some of the design parameters were modified to fit the installation, the unit performed to the design requirements over the full band and field of view.

References

Lerner, D. S., "A Wave Polarization Converter for Circular Polarization," *Trans. IEEE,* AP-13: January 1965, pp. 3–7.

Hacking, C. A., et al., "Man/Machine Design of a Broadband Microwave Circular Polarizer," *Second International Conference on System Sciences,* Hawaii (report of work performed at Stanford Research Institute in 1966), 1969.

Chapter

13

Validating the Prototype

The validation process described earlier in the text is required for the prototype. In addition, further testing is required to provide guidelines and data for production testing and evaluation.

13.1 VSWR Testing

The prototype should be VSWR-tested using a small sample lot (10 or more) of prototypes to verify unit-to-unit variation and limits in performance.

13.2 Preliminary Gain Testing

The prototype should be gain-tested without a polarizer, using a small sample lot of prototypes to verify unit-to-unit variations and limits in performance.

13.3 Pattern Coverage

At least two prototypes should be tested for principal and orthogonal polarization coverage in free-space and in the actual installation.

13.4 Gain

At least two prototypes with polarizers should be tested for principal and orthogonal polarization in free-space and in the actual installation.

13.5 Polarizers

The prototype polarizers should be axial-ratio-tested, using a single array element and several prototypes to verify unit-to-unit variations and limits in performance. By using a single element to verify polarizer performance, the test is more stringent because with a full array smoothing of performance results.

13.6 Matrices

The use of matrices is recommended for summarizing the results from the pattern coverage, gain, and polarizer tests.

13.7 Concluding Remarks

A pragmatic description of the prototype testing was provided. It should be readily extendable to similar design applications.

Chapter 14

Changeover to Production

Broadening design tolerances and defining minimum specifications should receive considerable attention when putting the design into production.

14.1 Broadening Design Tolerances

The microwave array considered previously will be used to illustrate the concept of broadening design tolerances. Figure 14.1 shows a photograph of the interior construction of the horn element used to form the microwave array. In the development process, earlier in the text, a tolerance study was undertaken. There, each of the principal elements constituting the design was evaluated to determine performance sensitivity. It was found that at least a ± 5 percent tolerance could be used in specifying manufacturing tolerances, so that casting of elements, if held to ± 5 percent, was allowed.

Upon completion, the cast array elements were assembled into an array and checked for VSWR and gain. Results showed acceptable performance, although there was a slight shift upward in frequency because width dimension changed slightly because of the casting process.

Next, the physical appearances of the cast elements were examined. In some cast elements, small (approximately $\frac{1}{16}$ in diameter) recessions were noted. Could these elements be used or would the small imperfections affect the design? From a performance viewpoint, it was felt that as long as there were no more than three imperfections per element, they were acceptable.

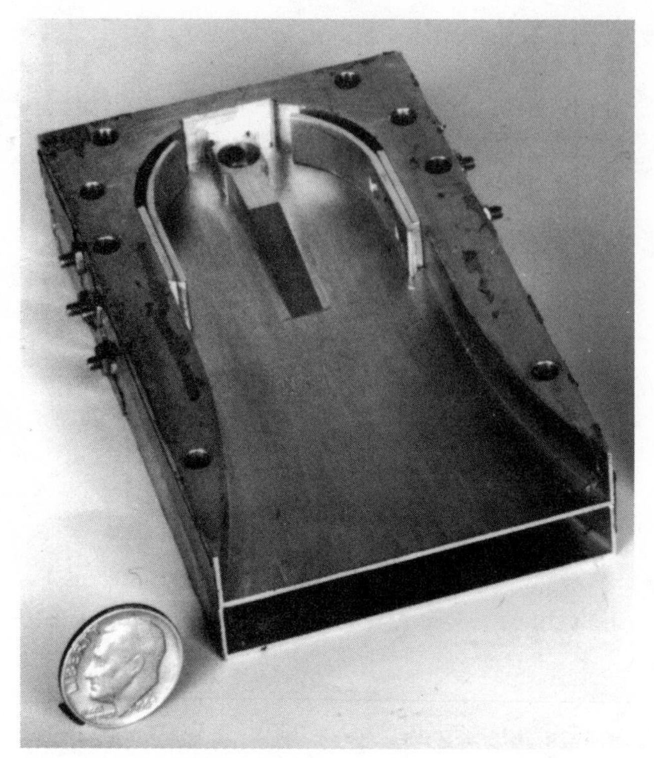

Figure 14.1 Ridged-horn inside layout (before casting). (*Courtesy of Raytheon Company*)

A more critical requirement was dictated by the final design use. There, because of possible contamination buildup, it was felt that the interior surfaces of an array element should be completely free of blemishes to be acceptable.

14.2 Defining Minimum Specifications

The production or manufacturing engineer is concerned with delivering a unit that meets specifications and, at the same time, gives the highest production yield.

It must be recognized that no matter how controlled the manufacturing process is, production units will always show some unit-to-unit variability.

Here, a sample group of 10 or more production units should be tested to the various specifications. Analysis of these data is then performed to set the minimum acceptable limits consistent with a good production yield (over 80 percent).

The process is illustrated using the test results from a group of production lenses. These lenses form the heart of the system design, because they are used to feed the transmit and receive arrays. All the lenses are tested for VSWR, insertion loss, array-factor gain, and electrical length through the center of the lens. VSWR is a standard test designed to verify soldering and connector integrity. Array-factor gain is the computed gain using automatic network analyzer derived data for the lens and assuming that all array elements are isotropic (that is, 0 dB gain). Insertion loss and array-factor gain are standard tests determined by the automatic network analyzer test. Electrical length, found by the automatic network analyzer test, verifies that the dielectric constant inside the lens is within specific limits.

The various data were then plotted into histogram charts. From these charts, the most probable values for each parameter were evident. The data were also catalogued into tables and most probable values and standard deviations were computed as shown in Appendix E.

Tables 14.1 through 14.3 show some of the results from these tests. Table 14.1 compares the most probable VSWR to the maximum noted VSWR at the low-frequency limit. Table 14.2 compares the most probable total insertion loss for the center and edge beamports. Table 14.3 displays the measured electrical lengths for the center ports across the lens.

TABLE 14.1 Most Probable Maximum VSWR and Maximum VSWR at F_{LOW} (5.0 GHz)

Beamport	Most probable maximum VSWR	Maximum VSWR
1	3:1	3.3:1
4	2.8:1	4.3:1
5	2.9:1	4.3:1
8	3:1	3.6:1

TABLE 14.2 Most Probable Total Insertion Loss

Frequency (GHz)	Outer beamports (dB)	Center beamports (dB)
5.0	3.8, 3.6	6.5, 6.5
6.8	3.0, 2.9	5.5, 5.2
8.5	2.4, 2.3	5.0, 4.9
13.9	1.3, 1.2	2.8, 2.8
18.0	2.7, 2.8	1.4, 1.4

TABLE 14.3 Electrical Length Center Ports (degrees at 18 GHz)

Lens S/N	BP 4 to AP 5	BP 5 to AP 4
71	2044	2040
72	2026	2031
74	2031	2026
76	2020	2032
77	2020	2032
78	2025	2017
81	2031	2024
82	2034	2029

Average electrical length = 2029°
Standard deviation = ±7.1°

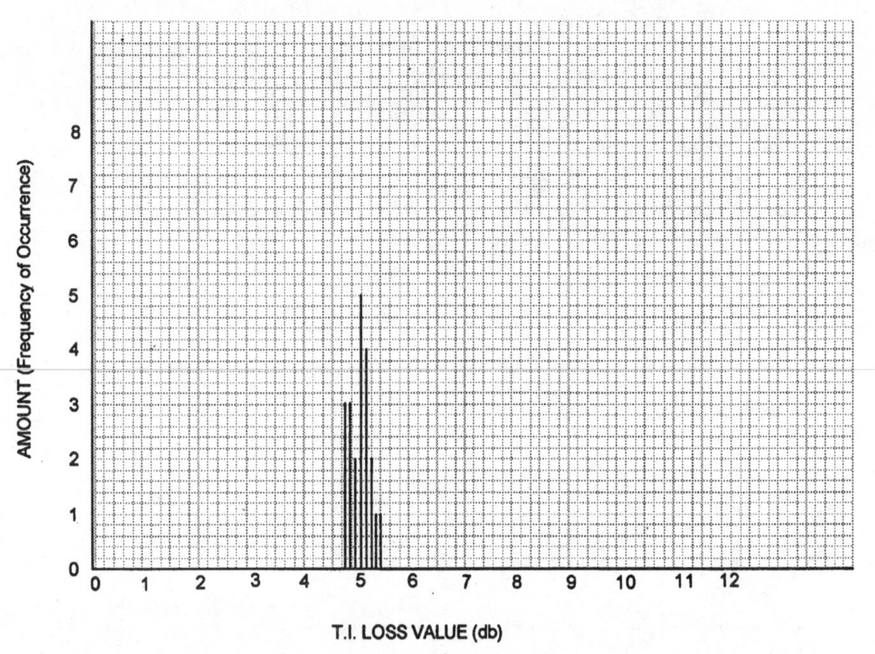

Figure 14.2 Lens total insertion loss, near-center beamport, $F = 8.5$ GHz.

Figure 14.2 shows a typical histogram of lens loss for the near-center beamport of the lens as found at 8.5 GHz. There the data are clustered about 5 dB. In this effort, a sample of 50 lenses was used so that results would be indicative of production runs.

This collection of data provides two classes of information. Class 1 represents written specifications. Their analysis is intended to reveal the extent of design margin. Class 2 represents those specifications required for the system. Their analysis is intended to reveal the performance margin.

14.3 Concluding Remarks

Understanding the needs of the manufacturing engineer is paramount in yielding high-percentage production runs. Here, the need for and means of imposing techniques were discussed and illustrated by examples.

Chapter

15

Validating the First Production Model

The first model that rolls off the assembly line requires a thorough validation process, incorporating all the tests described in Chap. 13. In addition, if possible, first-level system integration testing should be performed to ascertain how well the model will work in the system.

15.1 Engineering Testing and Evaluation

The validation process detailed in Chap. 13 should be conducted by a design engineering team to validate the first production model. Upon completion, the data should be entered into pass/fail matrices to determine compliance.

15.2 Factory Testing and Evaluation

The validation process detailed in Chap. 13 should be conducted by factory-test personnel, with some assistance from design staff, to validate the first production model. Here, the validation process translated from Chap. 13 guidelines will likely follow written test procedures. However, the tests may not be conducted in the same anechoic chamber. Different test equipment may be used with different computer programs.

All of these factors may result in somewhat different values for important specification parameters. These differences will need to be resolved by either analysis or additional testing. Test procedures and automated programs will need to be updated to reflect necessary changes. Then, critical tests will have to be rerun using these procedures to validate that production testing yields compliant results.

15.3 Concluding Remarks

Translating testing from engineering to factory test was described. The need for developing adequate test procedures was stressed.

Chapter

16

Production Testing

16.1 Introduction

Production testing represents a whole new dimension in the testing process. While the design engineer is concerned with examining every detail of the antenna design and the interaction of the parameters, the production engineer is concerned with how to guarantee the integrity of the product for the minimum cost per unit.

We shall consider production testing and how the design and production engineers must work together toward developing a low-cost, reliable test method.

16.2 VSWR Testing

A common way to validate the integrity of the design is to measure the VSWR. This test is simple to instrument. If a network analyzer is available, the test is readily programmable. Results are repeatable and pass/fail limits can be incorporated into the program. These procedures lead to a low-cost test method.

Now consider whether the VSWR test constitutes a reliable test for quality and compliance. If the antenna is used in a noncritical application only, the VSWR test is all that may be required. On the other hand, if the antenna is to be used where a stringent gain or sensitivity requirement exists, the VSWR test alone may not be adequate.

VSWR represents a measure of the transmission efficiency by measuring the reflected power. Passing a unit with a marginally acceptable VSWR could result in having the unit fail the gain or sensitivity test.

16.3 Sensitivity Testing

The purpose of this test is to ensure that the gain and sensitivity requirements will be met. The test measures the antenna response to incident field.

For the purpose of analysis, the antennas under consideration can be divided into two groups: low-gain antennas of less than 10 dB and high-gain antennas. To test high-gain antennas, a considerable separation between the transmit antenna and unit under test is required (i.e., a full-range or anechoic chamber). This group is thus excluded from further consideration. Low-gain antennas can be tested at much closer spacing to the transmit antenna to determine their approximate far-field gain (Monser, 1994).

16.4 Setting Up for VSWR and Gain Testing

Figure 16.1 shows a typical setup, which provides for both VSWR and gain testing. In this figure, the network analyzer simultaneously measures both parameters. VSWR, as taken, is the true value for the unit under test, while the received signal (which is approximately proportional to the gain of the unit under test for the far-field condition) may be comprised when using a small chamber. Nonetheless, this test will reveal any holes in the gain response and sensitivity over the frequency band.

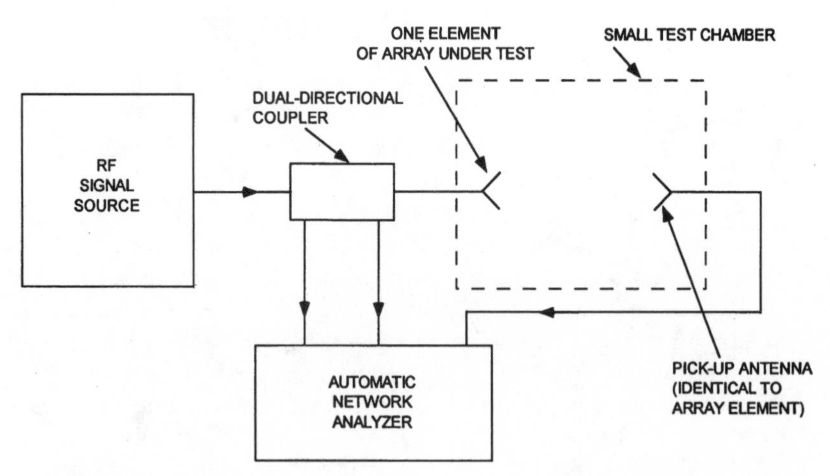

Figure 16.1 Production setup for simultaneously measuring VSWR and approximate gain.

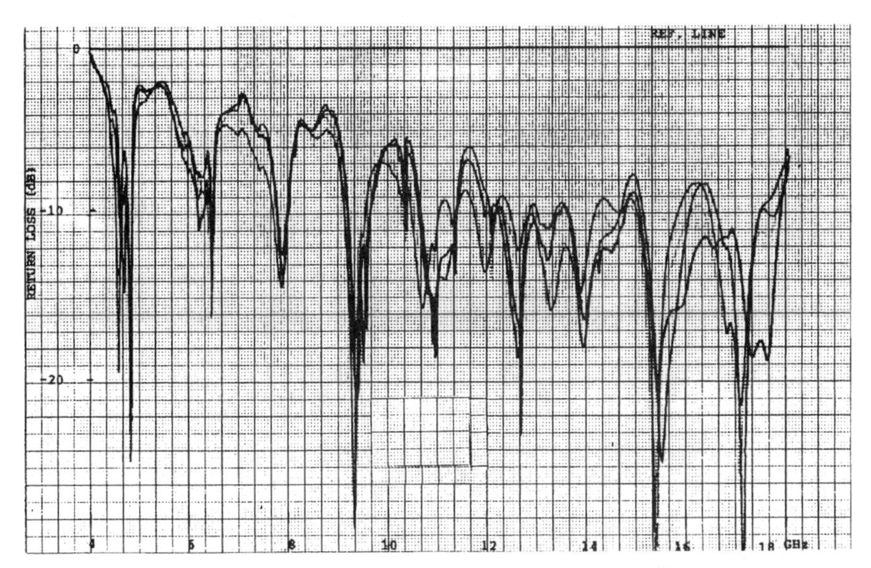

Figure 16.2 Passive VSWR, microwave horn array. (*Courtesy of Raytheon Company*)

16.5 Setting VSWR Limits

Figure 16.2 shows the VSWR response for the microwave array elements previously considered. The frequency band is divided into segments and pass/fail limits are added to the chart. Any value exceeding the level shown (i.e., return loss less than indicated) represents a failed condition.

16.6 Setting Gain Limits

Figure 16.3 shows the coupling from one of the microwave array elements to the pick-up antenna when tested in a small chamber. By testing a number of array elements and arrays, the segmented pass/fail limits can be set. Any value falling below the level shown represents a failed condition. This test also provides assurance that no gain holes exist, as shown in Fig. 16.3.

16.7 Concluding Remarks

An approach to production testing to ensure quality and compliance was given. This approach can be readily adapted to testing low-gain (i.e., under 10 dB) antennas.

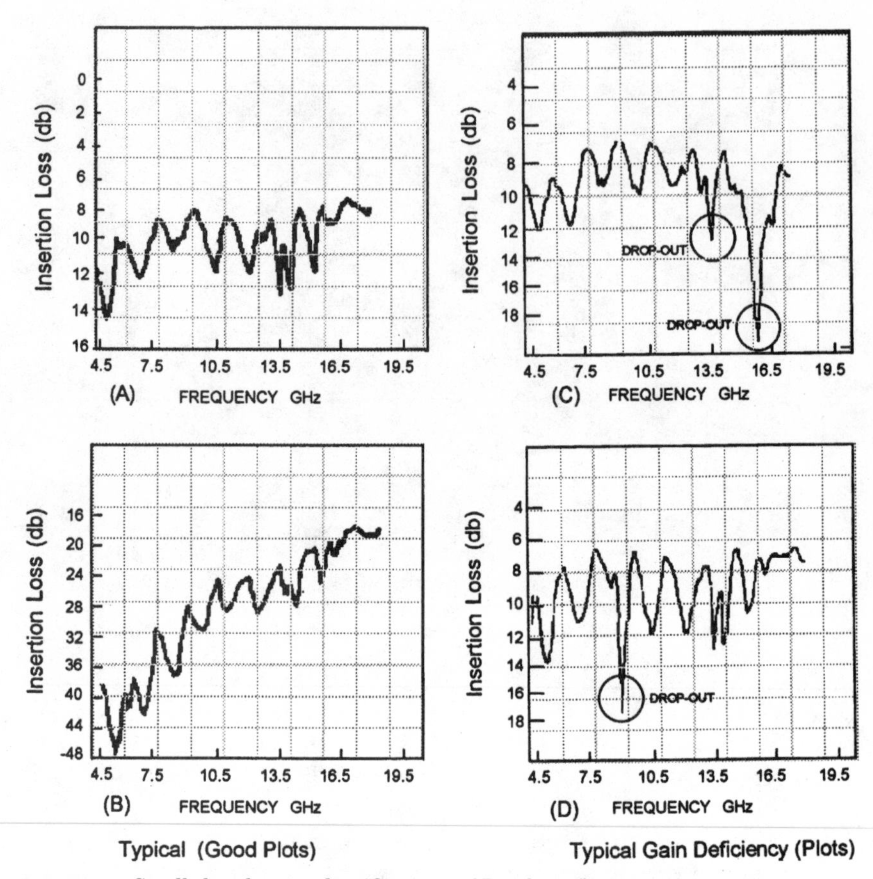

Figure 16.3 Small chamber results. (*Courtesy of Raytheon Company*)

Reference

Monser, George J., "Measure Antenna Gain Without a Test Range," *Microwaves & RF,* September 1994, pp. 113–114.

Chapter

17

Adapting to System Needs

Understanding the role of the antenna as it pertains to the system is important because the imposed specifications or requirements were derived from the system. As a consequence, there are two sets of requirements: those delineated by antenna specifications and those implicit in the system design. This chapter addresses antenna design guided by the system needs.

17.1 Working in Unison

The development of the antenna requirements depends upon the system's model and use. Figure 17.1 shows the elements of a system design. A receive array is used to cover the frequency band and field of view. Similarly, a transmit array is used to blanket the same field of view and frequency band. Each array uses a microwave lens to develop eight simultaneous beams over the field of view. In addition, two auxiliary functions must be provided. In receiving, it is preferable to cover the field of view instantaneously. In transmitting, the drive levels to the final amplifiers need to be known for optimum performance.

The simplest and preferred way to cover the same field of view and frequency band is by using identical arrays and lenses for both transmitting and receiving. Then the beams will be overlapping in space and a 1/1 coincidence will be achieved. The auxiliary receive function can be achieved by sampling the center receive element signal.[1] In

[1]When the array or lens has an even number of ports, then one closest to center can be used.

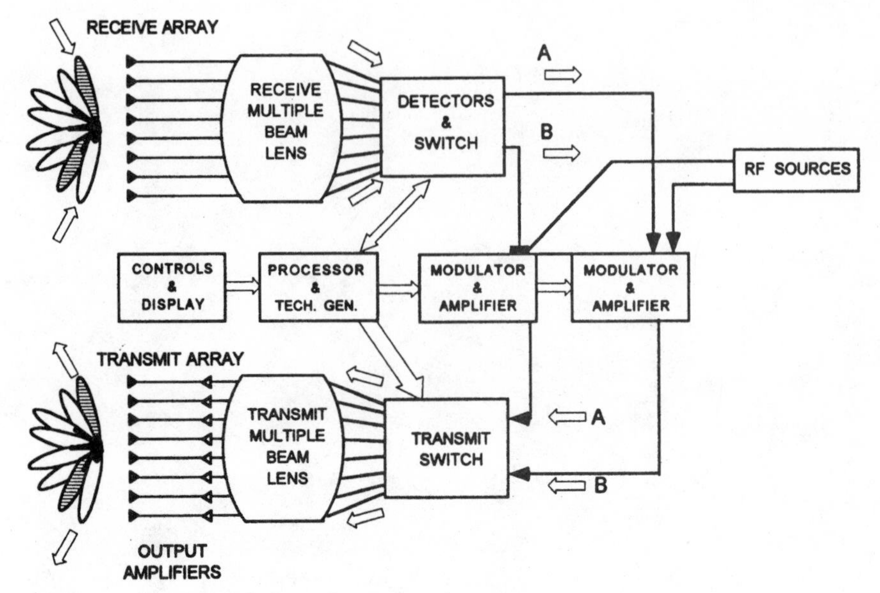

Figure 17.1 Receive and transmit antennas in system use.

transmission, the output from a center lens port can be sampled to determine drive level.

There is one additional benefit derived by using the same array for transmitting and receiving. If the external polarizers are of the same design, then the polarization characteristics over the field of view and frequency are identical.

17.2 Receive Antenna Subsystem

Figure 17.2 shows the receive antenna subsystem in accordance with the system design. Notice that a single directional coupler is added to allow instantaneous sampling over the full field of view. In addition, attenuators are inserted in all other receive-to-lens lines. The purpose of the attenuators is to taper the illumination and provide lower sidelobes than for uniform illumination (Monser, 1995). For successful operation, all attenuators and the directional coupler must be phase matched.

Figure 17.3 shows a set of beam patterns derived from the receive subsystem. By the choice of lens design, the beams remain fixed in space over the full frequency band. Also, beam splitting can be used to isolate the receive signal into a cell of approximately one-half the

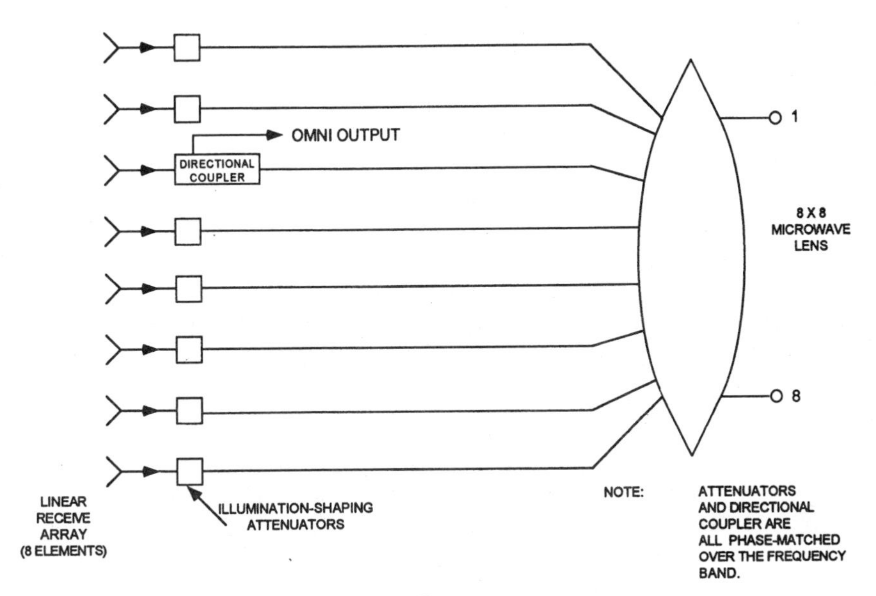

Figure 17.2 Receive subsystem with overall output.

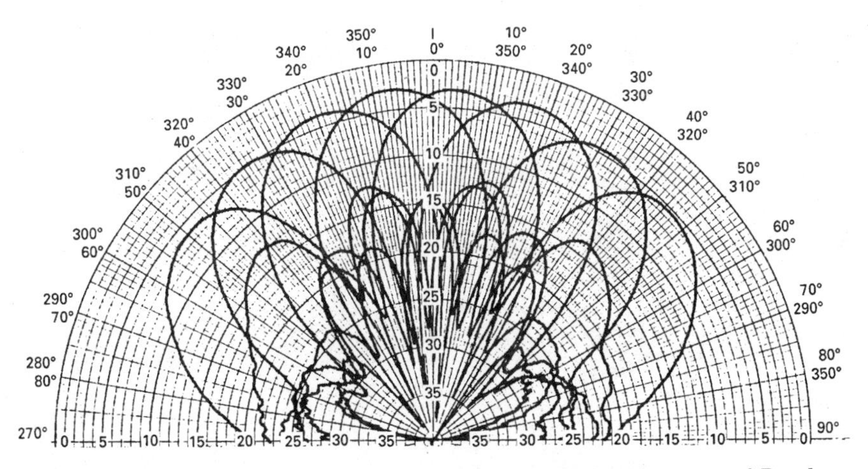

Figure 17.3 Receive subsystem beam patterns at 10 GHz. (*Courtesy of Raytheon Company*)

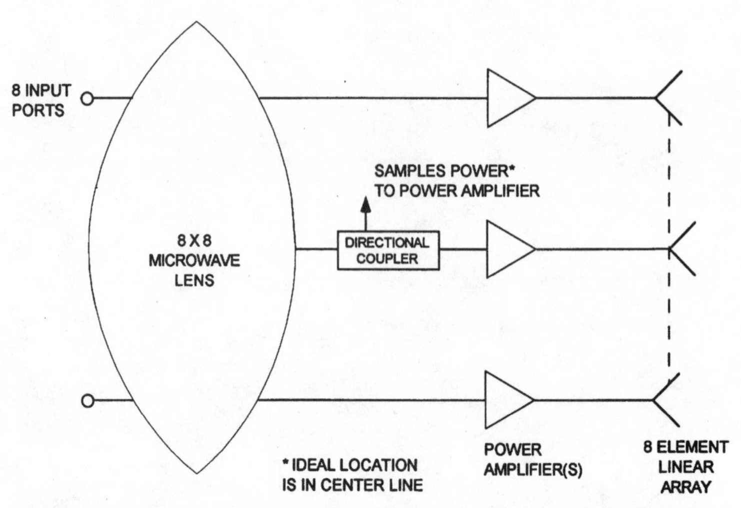

Figure 17.4 Transmit subsystem with sampler installed (simplified drawing).

3-dB beamwidth, so that more effective transmit power can be delivered on target.

17.3 Transmit Antenna Subsystem

Figure 17.4 shows elements of the transmit antenna subsystem. Notice that a single directional coupler is added to allow sampling the drive level to the near-center final TWTA to assure that nearly saturated power output results. Appendix F illustrates the condition for saturated power. The beam patterns developed in transmission are nearly identical to those in receive, except that the sidelobes are higher because nearly uniform illumination exists.

As noted in the receive design, beam splitting can be used. This is advantageous in transmit, for if the target falls close to a crossover between adjacent beams, the on-target power is reduced by 3 dB or 50 percent. This reduction in power can be minimized by using dual-beam excitation. To implement adjacent dual-beam operation, the system must be phase-matched from the input through the switch to all of the lens input ports. Then, beams can be formed in between such that, at adjacent beam crossovers, the loss of target power is on the order of 1 dB or about 20 percent.

17.4 Elements of the Design

The antenna arrays used in the aforementioned system were first described in Design Example 4.2 and Design Example 5.3. The care and quality of the lens were described under Production Testing in Chap. 16. Additional lens design information is given in the reference on page 91, where it is shown that the lens is an 8-input, 8-output lens utilizing Duroid substrate.

17.5 Concluding Remarks

Meeting the antenna requirements is important from a specifications viewpoint, but satisfying the system needs is also important. To be considered a success, any design must satisfy both. Goals to achieve this objective were illustrated by example.

Reference

Monser, George J., "A Reversible Rotman Lens Useful in Short, Linear Array Applications," *Microwave Journal,* January 1995, pp. 160–163.

Chapter

18

Unproven Designs and Remedies

This chapter should serve as a reminder that, no matter how elegant the mathematics, there is no substitute for a working model.

There exists a class of antennas that were designed properly, but failed to perform. Two examples of unproven designs are given and then solutions for each are illustrated.

18.1 Cavity-backed Spiral

Cavity-backed Archimedean and log-spiral antennas have been used extensively in wide-band receive applications. Figure 18.1 shows the layout of an Archimedean spiral antenna on a thin dielectric board. Radiation or reception coincides with the bands of the spiral that are equal to one wavelength in circumference, plus or minus about 10 percent. Thus the highest frequency corresponds to radiation or reception from a band of windings near the feed points. As the frequency is lowered, the radiation (or reception) band moves smoothly to the outer windings. Since the layout can cover multioctave wavelengths, the antenna is broad band and bidirectional, forming two lobes orthogonal to the spiral plane.

To change the pattern to a directional beam, the circuit board containing the spiral is mounted over a cavity, as shown in Fig. 18.2. For optimum operation, the spacing from the spiral surface to the back wall of the cavity should be kept to less than three-sixteenths of a

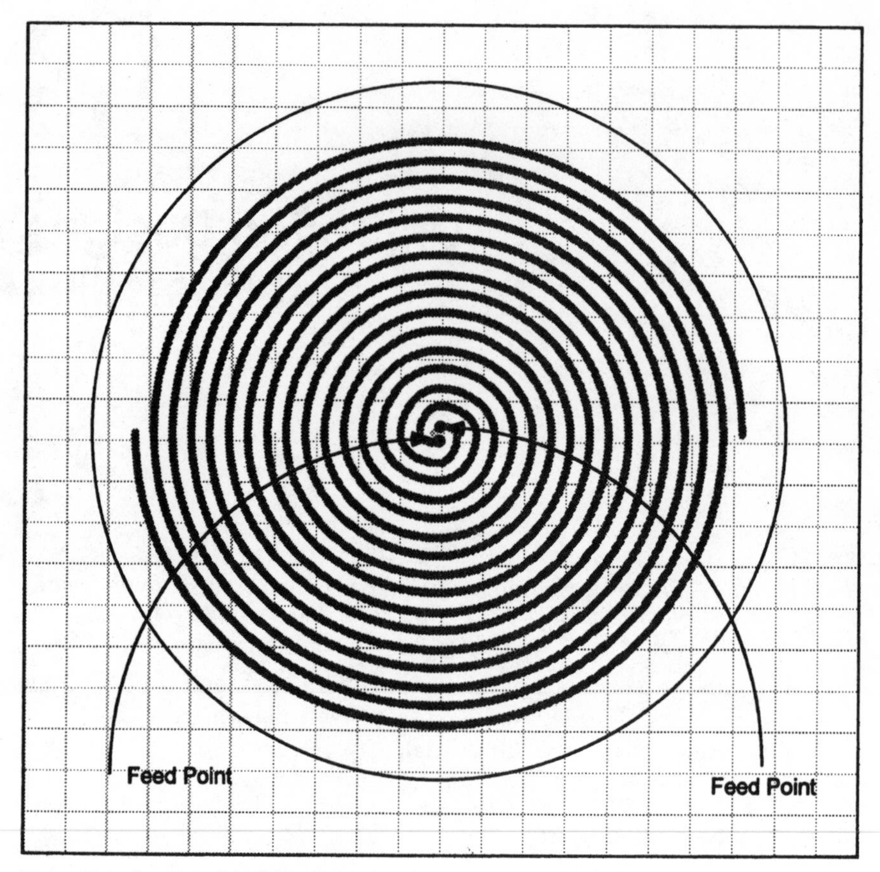

Figure 18.1 Layout of Archimedean spiral.

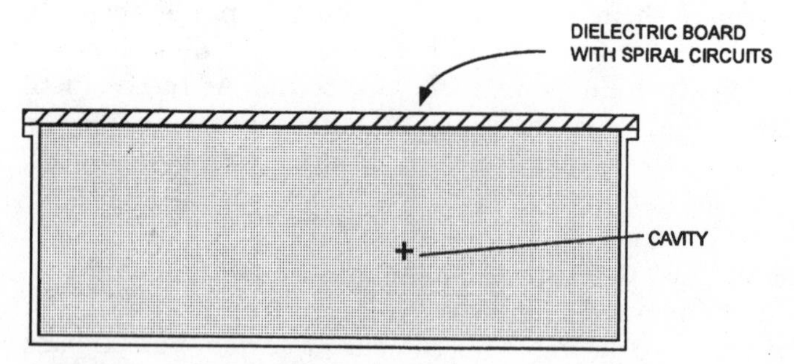

Figure 18.2 Archimedean spiral over cavity (cross section).

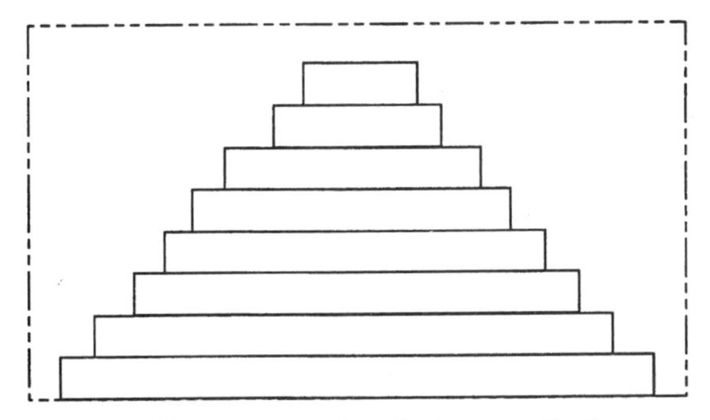

Figure 18.3 Reverse-stepped cavity (cross section).

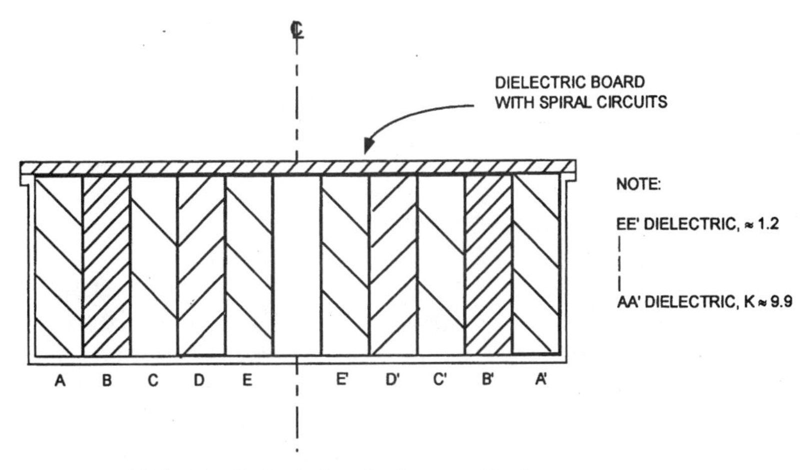

Figure 18.4 Dielectrically loaded cavity (cross section).

wavelength. The use of lossy materials in the cavity should be avoided so that gain loss is kept at a minimum.

Ideally, the back wall should be shaped to maintain an electrical spacing nearly constant with frequency. This leads to the back wall shape shown in Fig. 18.3 or, as an alternate configuration, to that shown in Fig. 18.4 where different dielectric values are used. Designs similar to those shown in Figs. 18.3 and 18.4 failed to pass the pattern performance where smooth, monotonic patterns were required.

Figure 18.5 shows a cross section of the cavity that has found wide application in broad band spiral design. This type of design, in contrast to conventional design, yields smooth patterns over an approximately 3/1 frequency band. Next, to visualize why this design works,

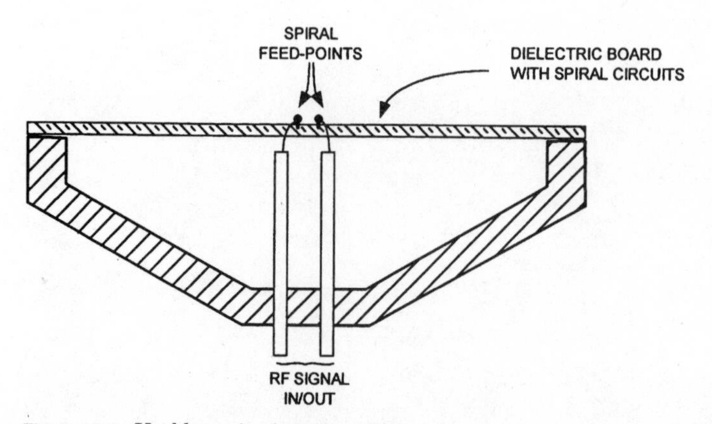

Figure 18.5 Usable cavity (cross section).

consider operation near the low-frequency end of the band. There, reflections from the sloping cavity walls form a single-lobe pattern. These patterns are maintained through midband. As the radiation band approaches the feed points, the high band windings act as a feed for the entire cavity. The patterns narrow somewhat, but they remain single lobed and smooth.

The other aspect in this design is concerned with the feed lines. Ideally, a split-tapered balun can be used to feed the spiral. However, it has been found in practice that not using a balun works just about as well, yielding under 3/1 VSWR and acceptable patterns. The simple connection shown in Fig. 18.6 is adequate for most applications.

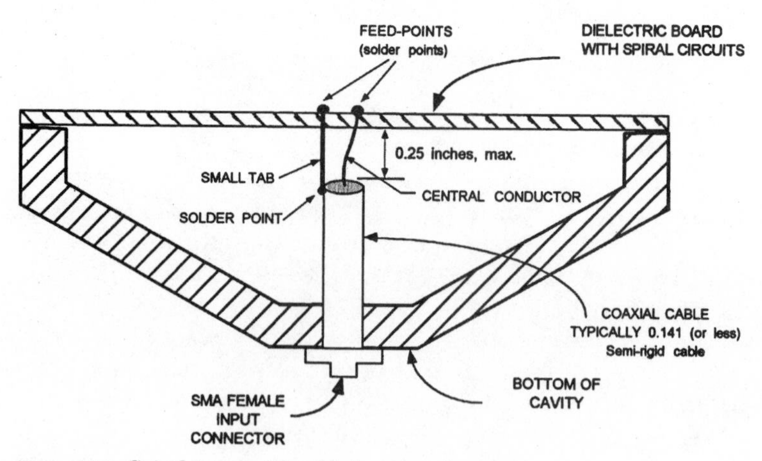

Figure 18.6 Spiral input without balun transformer.

Figure 18.7 Printed notch subarray.

18.2 Microwave Array

Another way to form circular polarization with the microwave array described earlier is to incorporate an orthogonal polarization in each array element and then to excite the pair of orthogonal array elements using a 90° hybrid. This mechanization offers potentially both senses of circular polarization by feeding either hybrid input, in contrast to one sense of circular polarization (using the array with an external polarizer).

It appeared that the orthogonal polarization could be provided by simply placing a printed notch subarray circuit board in each array element, as depicted in Fig. 18.7. Notch designs of 3 and 4/1 bandwidths were available. On centerline, the circuit board should have minimal effect on the array horns.

The configuration shown in Fig. 18.7 was tried and found deficient. The notch subarray functioned as expected over the band, but the horn elements developed several gain dropouts over the band.

Figure 18.8 shows one solution where both the horn and the stripline elements performed satisfactorily over multioctave bandwidth. This arrangement has one drawback and that is, when forming circular polarizations, the axial ratio deteriorated with wide scan angles because of the separation in the phase centers of the dual-elements.

Figure 18.9 shows various test models illustrating the preferred solution in which the stripline elements are on the horn centerlines.

Figure 18.8 Integrated printed notch subarray. (*Courtesy of Raytheon Company*)

Since the phase centers are closer together, better axial ratios are maintained over the field of view. In order to make this design work, the stripline circuits were suspended inside the horn elements to remove gain dropouts resulting from side wall currents. Recall that traps were used to remove a singular dropout for the horn array when first considered. By suspending the striplines no path existed for sidewall currents (i.e., no gain dropouts for the horns).

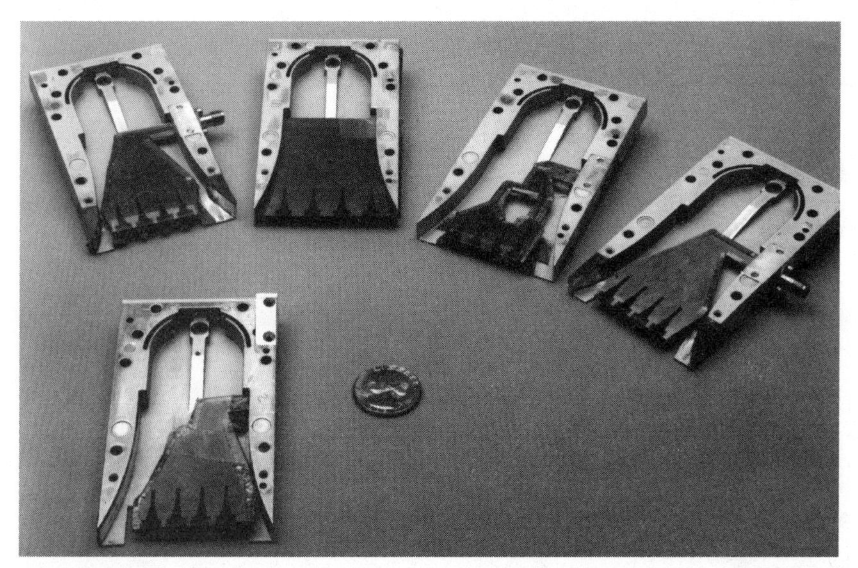

Figure 18.9 Stripline elements on horn centerline (test models). (*Courtesy of Raytheon Company*)

Chapter

19

Patenting Your Antenna

Antennas that are unique should be patented, particularly if they have profit potential. The steps in the patenting process are

- Preliminary search
- Filing a preliminary disclosure
- Filing a patent application
- Supporting patent claims
- Receiving the patent

19.1 Preliminary Search

Once the design is proven, it is necessary to search the literature to make sure that the design is unique, wholly or in part. The design is unique if it reports at least one aspect not previously disclosed and the feature is not obvious to other skilled practitioners.

19.2 Filing a Preliminary Disclosure

The key elements in this disclosure are

- Statement and discussion of problem
- Description of invention (how it works)
- Identification of novel features
- Potential usage

Each of the aforementioned points needs to be covered in detail in the disclosure by the inventor or inventors. In addition, the disclosure should be written in concise, clear language. The single most important part of the process is to identify clearly the potential usage of the invention.

19.3 Filing a Patent Application

The formal patent application is best prepared by a patent attorney. The patent attorney will use the information given in the preliminary disclosure, but he or she will need to translate it to patent format (legal language).

During the preparation of the application, the attorney will, most likely, ask for clarifications and different ways to express meanings. Upon completion of the patent application, the patent attorney will give a copy to the inventor for review and make corrections if necessary. The proposed corrections should be discussed with the attorney. After the review is done and corrections are made, the application is ready to file with the patent office.

19.4 The Patent Office

The patent office reviews the patent application for acceptance. The examiner will then cite other patents to be reviewed before acceptance and identify the proposed allowable claims. Upon receipt of this information, the inventor would review the other patents in order to identify novel features of the proposed invention. The submitted claims (generally all-encompassing) are compared to the proposed allowable claims and adjusted accordingly.

Appendix G details a typical patent process from disclosure to receiving the patent.

19.5 Concluding Remarks

The steps to be followed in patenting a design were given. These steps are generic and readily extendable to other designs.

Chapter

20

Wrap-Up

This book was written to serve the system engineer, the antenna engineer, and the production supervisor in acquiring a better understanding of antennas. Design examples were given to illustrate the design process. Flow-through paths were developed to show the transition from the engineering model to production, including a description of production disciplines.

Throughout the work, hard models were used rather than computer models for two reasons: expediency and because installation effects are more readily approximated with hard models. While the guidelines were given for specific design examples, they can with some changes be extended to cover other designs.

Remember, no matter how elegant the mathematics, there is no substitute for a working model to support the design.

Appendix

Power Test Setup

A.1 Introduction

Each component in the transmit antenna subsystem that will be exposed to RF power should be tested prior to use. This appendix describes how the power testing of the four-element, stripline notch subarray shown in Fig. 7.3 was conducted. The tests were designed to reveal the safe and upper limits of stripline circuits in Duroid 5880 under cw power up to 100 W at 12 GHz, for altitudes from 1000 to 70,000 ft, over an ambient temperature range from 20° to 125°C.

A.2 Test Articles

Figure A.1 shows a photograph of the two antenna test fixtures. The aluminum test fixture allowed determination of the safe power handling under heat-sink conditions by clamping the smooth aluminum surface (opposite side from screw heads) to an aluminum plate for thermal stability during test. The other test fixture shown was built in NEMA, G-10, a dielectric offering poor thermal transfer and maximum stress conditions.

A.3 Conduct of Test

Figure A.2 shows the basic instrumentation for conducting the tests. All tests were conducted with the samples in a chamber where various temperature and altitude conditions could be simulated. Forward and return power from the sample were monitored. Also, through-line power and radiated signal from the antenna samples were monitored.

Figure A.1 Test fixtures for power test. (*Courtesy of Raytheon Company*)

Thermocouples were placed at various locations on the test sample, along the RF chain, and on the aluminum within the chamber; another heat sink was suspended within the chamber.

The following sequence is typical:

1. First, the test sample connectors were inspected and cleaned (if necessary).
2. Next, the sample was lightly coated with thermal grease and clamped to the aluminum heat-sink block inside the chamber. Here, a dielectric block was positioned between the upper clamp and the sample so that (mainly) one thermal transfer path was provided.
3. RF connections were then made for the power measurements.
4. Various thermocouples were placed in position.
5. Temperature–altitude equilibrium was established within the chamber.
6. RF input power was applied and increased incrementally for various time intervals.
7. Monitoring of all sensors, including time, was performed.

In each test sequence, the test was taken to thermal equilibrium for the safe power determination or until failure for the stress–limit tests.

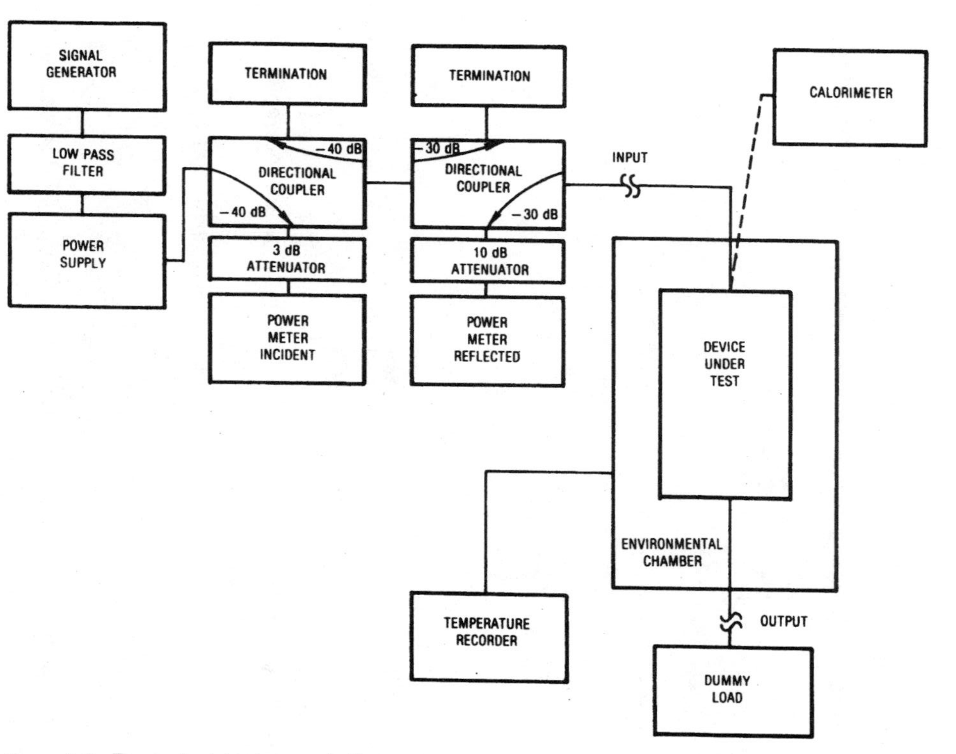

Figure A.2 Power test instrumentation.

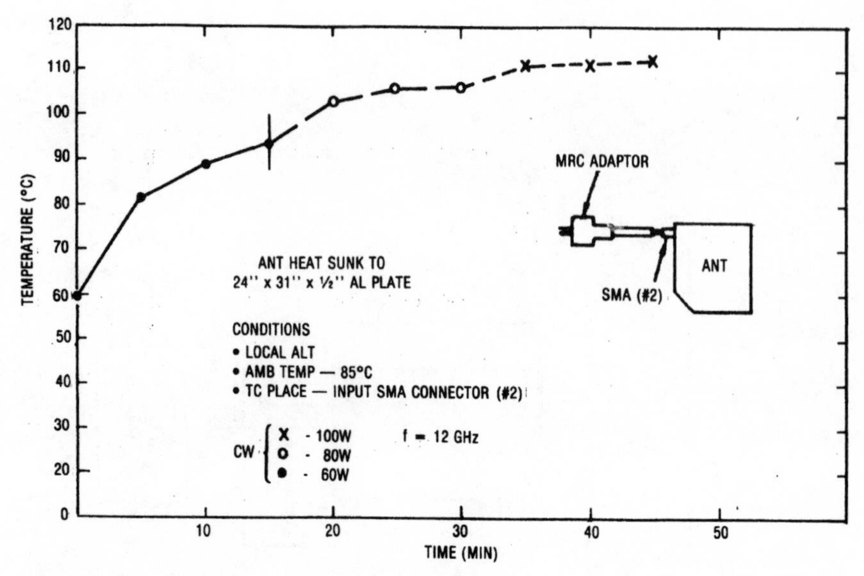

Figure A.3 Temperature vs. time profile, 1000-ft altitude (aluminum fixture). (*Courtesy of Raytheon Company*)

A.4 Results

Figure A.3 shows the observed temperature versus time profile for the antenna in an aluminum fixture at 1000-ft altitude and ambient temperature 85°C as the applied 12 GHz, cw, RF power increases from 60 to 100 W. Result: no failures.

Figure A.4 shows a repeat of the prior test at 50,000 ft. Result: no failures.

Figure A.5 shows a repeat of the first test at 70,000 ft. Result: no failures.

Figure A.6 shows a repeat of the last test at 70,000 ft and ambient temperature of 110°C. Result: failure noted.

New circuit boards and input connectors were used to replace the failed parts and the tests were rerun. Again, failure occurred in the last test.

Figure A.7 shows the disintegration of a connector experienced in a maximum stress test sequence of the antenna sample in the G-10 holding fixture (no heat sink).

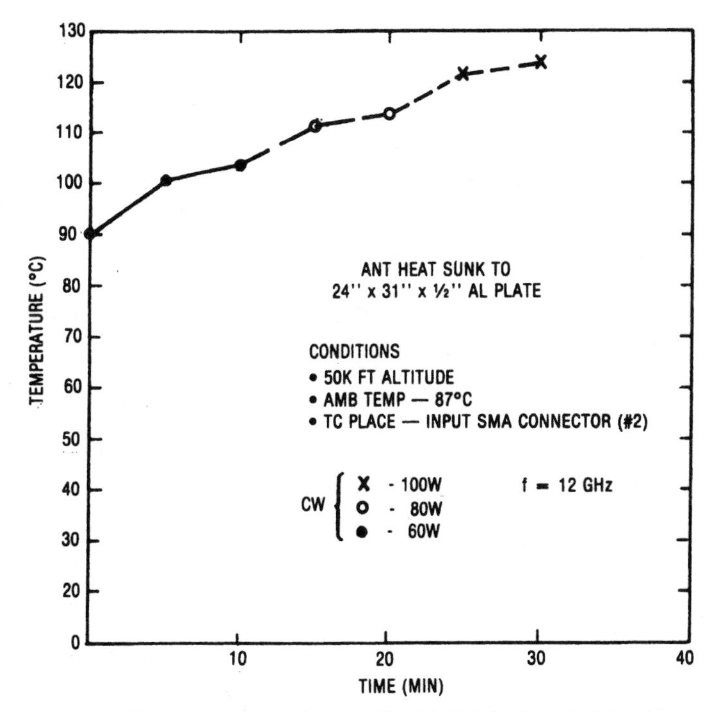

Figure A.4 Temperature vs. time profile [50,000-ft altitude (aluminum fixture)]. (*Courtesy of Raytheon Company*)

A.5 Analysis

Center conductor temperatures were estimated by calculations for three cases of stripline failure, using temperature measured at the input 3-mm connector, estimated power dissipations, and steady-state analysis for simplicity.

Results indicated that two of the observed failures were probably temperature related in that the predicted center-conductor temperatures exceeded, by 50 percent, the rated maximum temperature of 200°C. In one test, at 70,000 ft, failure was observed to occur with the calculated center conductor at 160°C. By inspection after test, it was confirmed that this failure was voltage related.

A.6 Concluding Remarks

This appendix has presented a benchmark on the safe power handling of 50-Ω circuits in Duroid 5880 manufactured by the Rogers Corporation, Chandler, AZ.

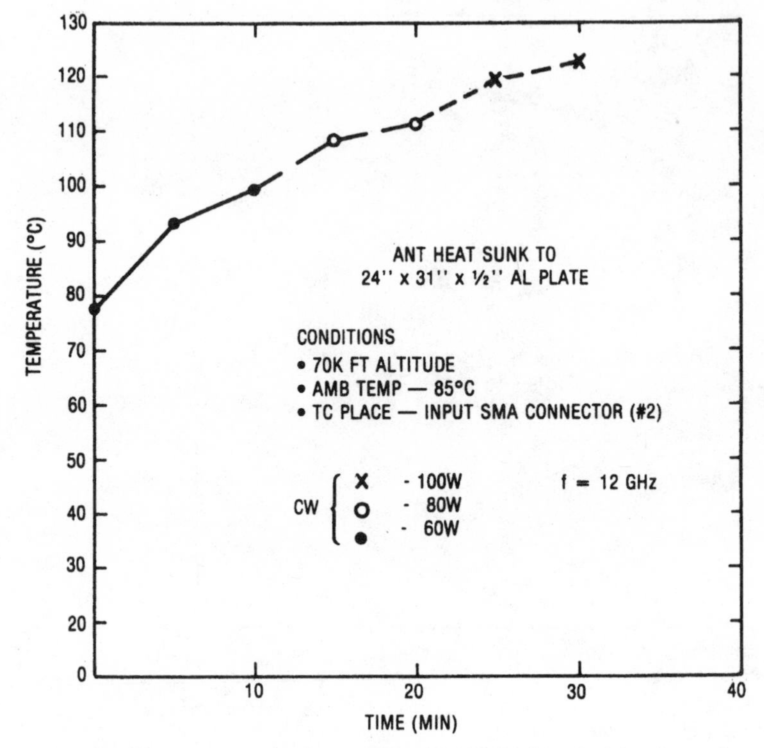

Figure A.5 Temperature vs. time profile, 70,000-ft altitude (aluminum fixture). (*Courtesy of Raytheon Company*)

By careful attention in assembly to avoid air gaps and contaminants and with heat-sink provisions to limit temperature rise from 85° to 100°C, 50-Ω stripline circuits in Duroid 5880 should safely handle 50 W of cw power up to 12 GHz and altitudes up to 70,000 ft.

Input VSWRs under 2/1 for the component under test are recommended to minimize voltage-related failures at high altitudes.

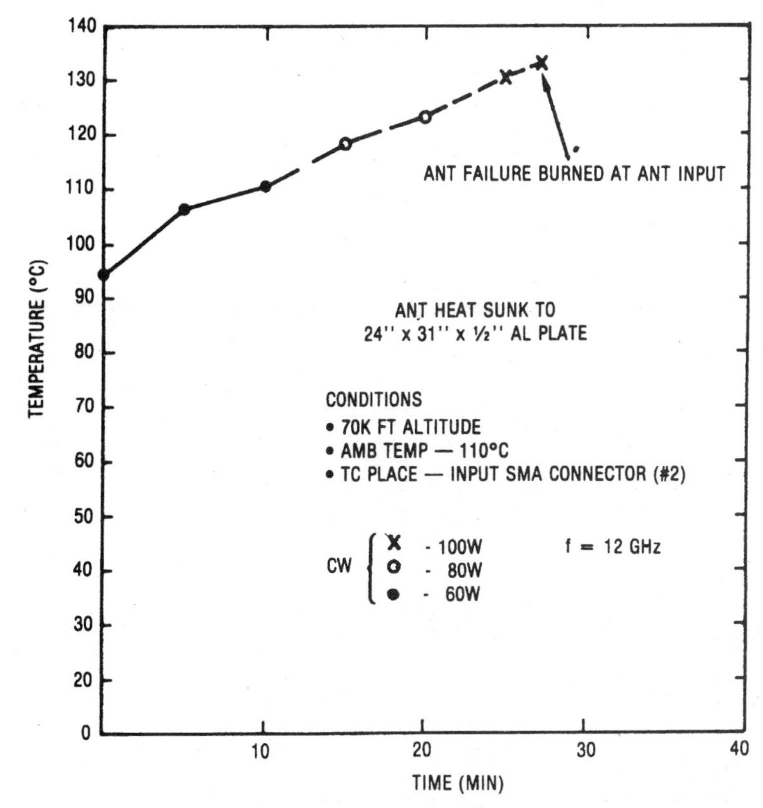

Figure A.6 Temperature vs. time profile, 70,000-ft altitude (aluminum fixture; maximum stress test, 110°C ambient). (*Courtesy of Raytheon Company*)

Figure A.7 Disintegrated connector, 70,000-ft altitude, 110°C ambient, maximum stress. (*Courtesy of Raytheon Company*)

Appendix

B

Determining Active VSWR

B.1 Introduction

This appendix describes how to calculate the active VSWR.

B.2 Active VSWR

Active VSWR provides a measure of the power transmission efficiency when all elements in the array are simultaneously driven. It is composed of two components: the passive VSWR and the coupled energy from the other elements of the array. The formulation is accomplished by measuring the complex passive reflection coefficient and the complex total coupling from all elements to the element under test.

Figure B.1 shows the generic test steps using a network analyzer capable of measuring S_{11} and S_{12}. S_{11} is the complex passive reflection coefficient for the element under test. S_{12} is the complex coupling between any element to the element under test. The total complex coupling T_c is found as the summation of the individual couplings to the element under test.

Figures B.2 and B.3 illustrate two cases for active reflection. In Fig. B.2, the interaction of coupling and passive reflection yields an active reflection lower than the passive reflection. In Fig. B.3, the same interaction produces a larger active reflection than the passive reflection. In each instance, the active VSWR is found by using

Determing Active VSWR

1.Select an array element for test.

2.Measure the passive reflection coefficient.

3.Measure,in succession,the complex coupling from the element under test to each element.

4.Find the total complex coupling coefficient.

5.Plot the passive reflection and total coupling coefficient to a common reference.

6.Find the active reflection coefficient (completes the triangle).

7.Compute active VSWR= $\frac{1+|\Gamma_A|}{1-|\Gamma_A|}$

where:

$|\Gamma_A|$ **= magnitude of the active reflection coefficient.**

Figure B.1 Automatic network analyzer, setup for active VSWR test.

$$\text{Active VSWR} = \frac{1 + |\Gamma_A|}{1 - |\Gamma_A|}$$

where $|\Gamma_A|$ = the absolute value of the active reflection coefficient

B.3 Concluding Remarks

Two cases for active reflection were illustrated. In the first case, a lower active VSWR resulted when the passive and coupled vectors were combined. In the second case, the cancellation effect between the passive and coupled vectors did not occur.

In the design of an array for optimum transmission efficiency (low active VSWR), it is necessary to understand the relationships that exist by either designing for the lowest passive VSWR or making use of the cancellation effect, whichever is more appropriate.

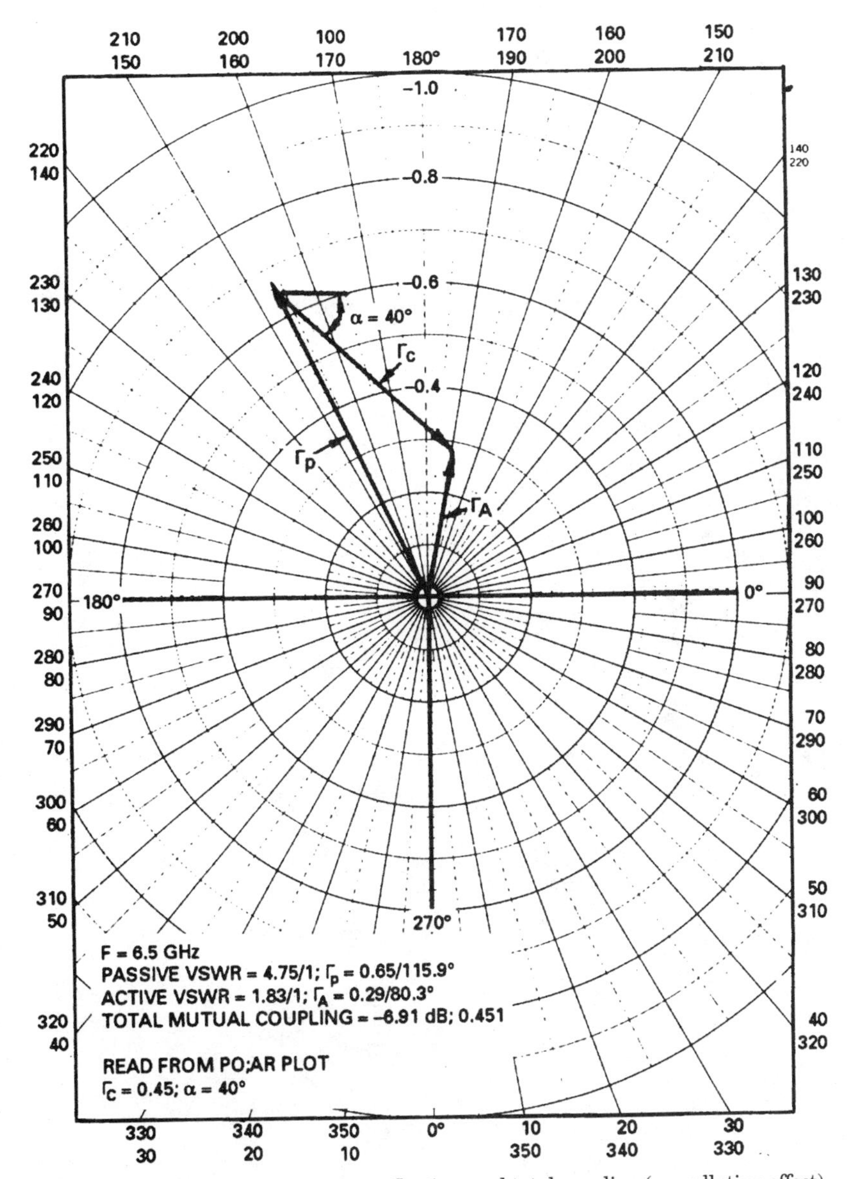

Figure B.2 Active reflection, passive reflection, and total coupling (cancellation effect).

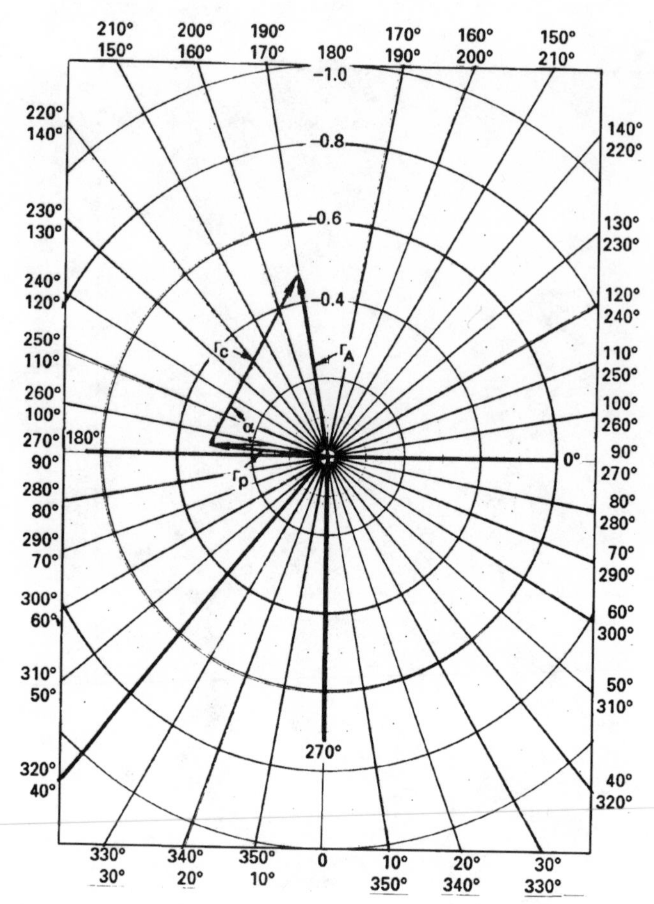

Figure B.3 Active reflection, passive reflection, and coupling (noncancelling effect).

Appendix

C

Calibrating a Gain Standard

C.1 Introduction

Typically, gain standards cover approximately one-half octave in frequency, so if the planned test extends several octaves, then a number of standards must be used. And although each gain standard is calibrated, two different values of gain may result for the unit under test at each crossover point between standards. A multioctave gain standard avoids the crossover uncertainties and expedites testing.

C.2 A Broadband Horn for Calibration

Figure C.1 shows a sketch of a dual-polarized horn that covers several octaves (2 to 18 GHz). The horn was first manufactured by EM Systems. The horn is currently available from Watkins-Johnson, Palo Alto, CA. VSWR for each input is excellent over the full band from 2 to 18 GHz. This appendix shows how to calibrate the horn.

C.3 Calibration Technique

One of the simplest calibration techniques is to test pairs of several nearly identical horns (if available) from transmitter to receiver. Figure C.2 shows the test arrangement. The following parameters are measured:

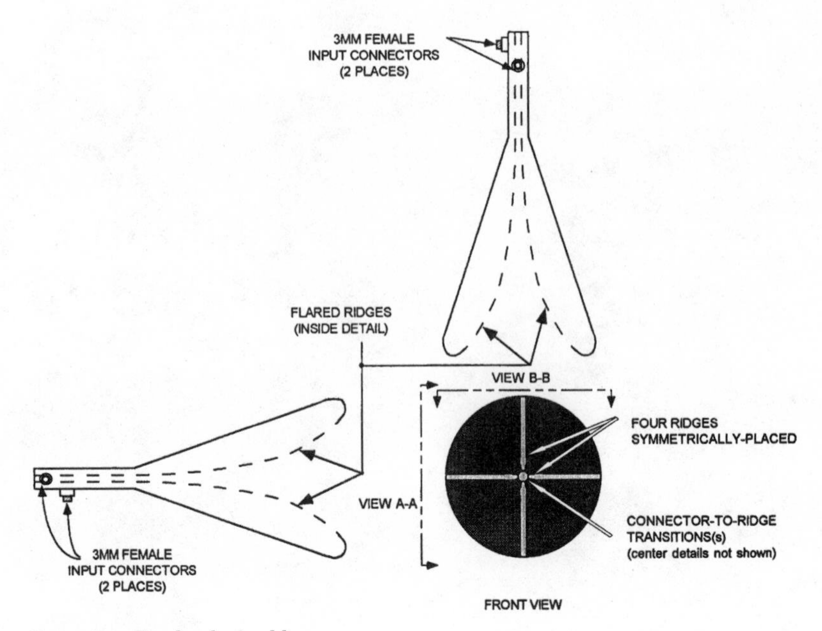

Figure C.1 Dual-polarized horn.

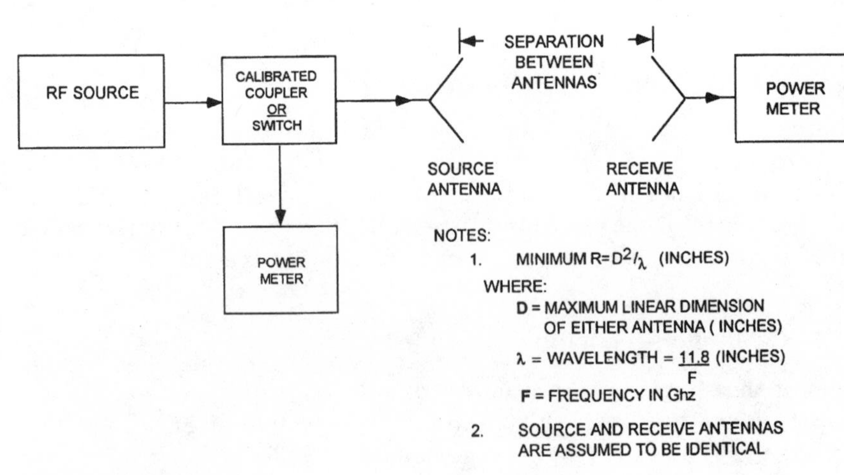

Figure C.2 Setup for gain.

Antenna gain and separation are linked by:

$$R = 2D^2/\lambda$$

where:
R= the distance between antennas for far field to apply,
D= the maximum linear dimension either antenna,
λ= wavelength=c/f,
c = the velocity of light,
f = the operating frequency.

Antenna aperture and gain are linked by:

$$G = 4\pi A/\lambda^2$$

where:
G= the antenna gain,
A= the aperture area,which is D-squared for a square aperture and D-squared / 4 for a circular aperture.

Using Friis equation for free space propagation and rearranging terms yields:

$$G_T G_R = (P_R/P_T)(\lambda/4\pi R)^2,$$

so if the power ratio is found and terms λ and R are known then the antenna gain is readily found for like antennas as the square-root of the gain product.

Figure C.3 Gain formulas and relationships.

- Power into transmit horn
- Received power
- Aperture-to-aperture separation
- Frequency (i.e., wavelength)

Then, applying the Friis free-space equation (see Fig. C.3), the gain product for the transmit/receive horns is found. And, since the horns were assumed identical, the individual horn gain is readily found. Figure C.4 shows plotted data derived by testing pairs of horns.

C.4 Concluding Remarks

A simple and reliable gain calibration procedure (which avoids cross-over uncertainties introduced when multiple gain standards are used) was described.

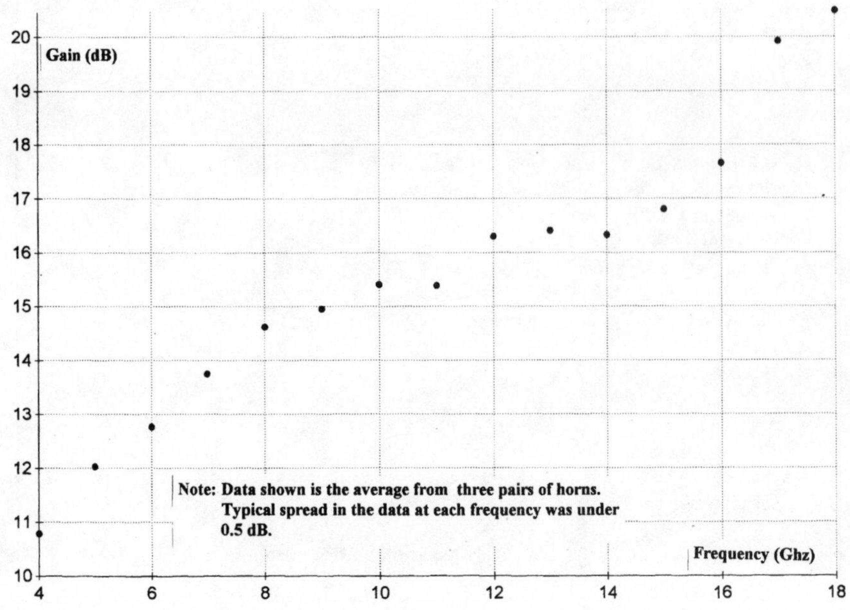

Figure C.4 Gain plots from three pairs of horns.

Appendix

D

Meanderline Polarizer

D.1 Introduction

The meanderline polarizer, first developed by the Stanford Research Institute, Menlo Park, CA, in 1966, has found wide application with excellent polarization-changing ability over more than an octave and over a $120° \times 120°$ field of view.

This appendix describes design details for a polarizer for a power application up to 100 W/in^2, at a maximum ambient temperature of 125°C, and altitudes up to 50,000 ft.

D.2 Basic Meanderline Design

Figure D.1 shows one sheet depicting the elements of the design. When the electric field incident on the meanderlines is displaced 45° from the meanderline, the effect upon the field components shown is to produce a phase displacement between components of approximately 15 electrical degrees. If six identical sheets spaced one-fourth wavelength apart are used, then a total phase delay of 90° is achieved (i.e., circular polarization). Measured boresight performance shows that a six-sheet polarizer exhibits two excellent points of axial ratio, similar to that displayed in Fig. D.2. In the scan-plane, the axial ratios remain acceptable to $\pm 50°$ from the normal (i.e., boresight). However, between $\pm 50°$ and $\pm 60°$, the axial ratios can degrade to 7 to 9 dB.

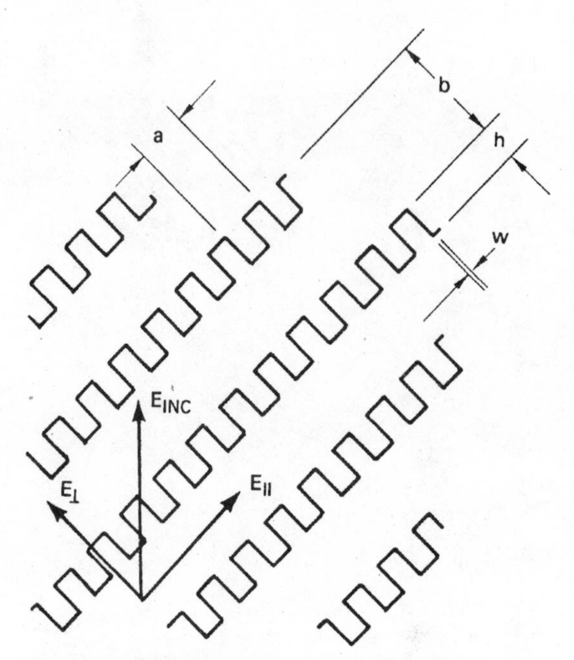

Figure D.1 Meanderline polarizer layout, design parameters illustrated (see SRI reference for values).

D.3 Transmit Polarizer

Figure D.3 shows a sketch of how the transmit polarizer can be constructed to handle the power. In this design, the meanderlines are printed on thin sheets of low-loss dielectric, such as Duroid 5880 manufactured by the Rogers Corporation. Pairs of sheets are supported by a low-loss honeycomb. Air spaces are provided between each sandwich for convection and conduction to improve power handling. In addition, each sheet is covered with a 1- to 3-mil low-loss coating for environmental protection and to minimize meanderline oxidation.

Because of space (installation limits), two deviations from the preferred design configuration are required. The height dimension should have been extended farther. When built, some spillover in the elevation plane may occur in front of the microwave array. The second deviation occurred in the scan plane (around the ends of the array) where only one-eighth wavelength spacing between the sheets would fit the installation.

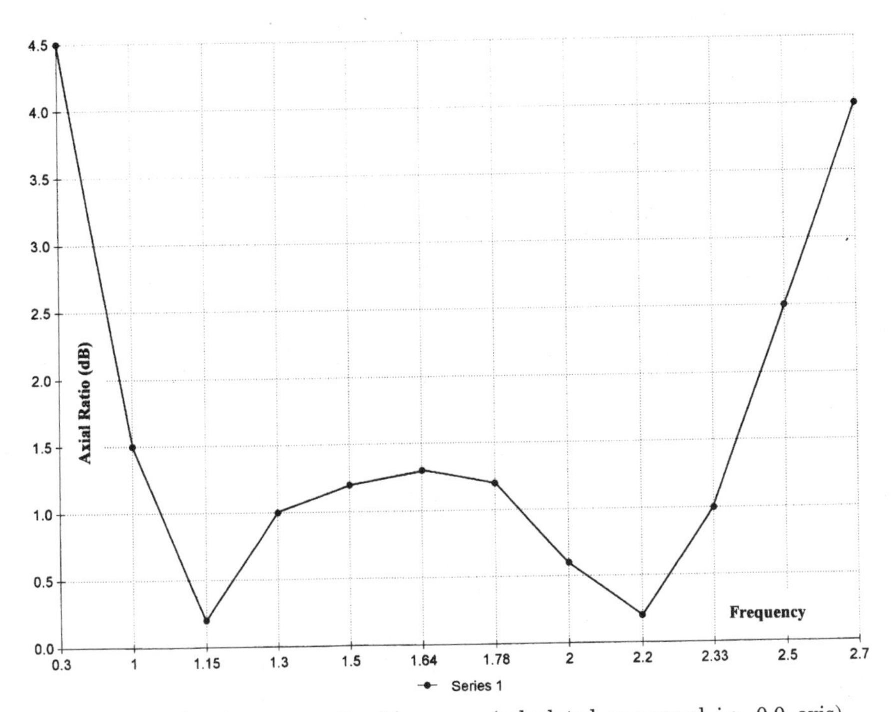

Figure D.2 Axial ratio vs. normalized frequency (calculated, on normal, i.e., 0,0–axis).

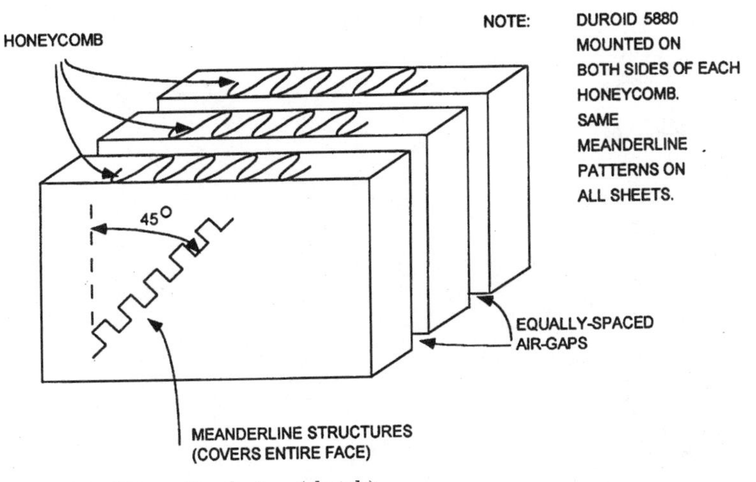

Figure D.3 Transmit polarizer (sketch).

D.4 Test Results

When the polarizer was tested, the axial ratios were within specified limits over the space rectangle of 120° × 30° in elevation. Over 80 percent of the field of view and 80 percent of the bandwidth from 5 to 18 GHz, the axial ratios were 6 dB or less. Over the remaining sector and near the band limits, some axial ratios of 7 to 9 dB were found.

Power handling under temperature and altitude was verified by test. These tests indicated the polarizer would safely handle cw power of 100 W/in^2.

Appendix

E

Production Tolerance Analysis

E.1 Introduction

Fifty 8 × 8 lenses were built and tested using an automatic network analyzer to obtain the requirement parameters for the production test requirement specification.

E.2 Lens Construction

The lens construction used Duroid 5880 single registration and contained no dummy ports or lossy materials.

E.3 Performance Parameters

All lenses were tested for VSWR, insertion loss, array-factor gain and electrical length through the center of the lens. VSWR is a standard test designed to verify soldering and connector integrity. Insertion loss and array-factor gain are standard lens performance parameters determined by the *automatic network analyzer* (ANA) measurement. Electrical length is used to verify that the Duroid 5880 dielectric constant is within specified limits.

E.4 Data Analysis

The various data were plotted in histogram charts. From these charts, the most probable value for each parameter was evident. The data were then catalogued into tables and the most probable values and standard deviations computed.

E.5 Results

Table E.1 shows the most probable maximum VSWR for several beamports at F_{LOW}.

Table E.2 shows the most probable array-factor gain.

Table E.3 shows the most probable total insertion loss.

Figure E.1 shows a sample of the histograms used in compiling Tables E.1 through E.3.

Table E.4 shows the results of the electrical length measurement for 10 lenses.

Table E.5 shows the standard deviation 1−Σ for the array-factor gain.

Table E.6 shows the standard deviation for the total insertion loss.

Figure E.2 shows total insertion loss plotted versus frequency.

E.6 Concluding Remarks

The sample size of 50 lenses assured that the production tolerances found and used in the production lens test specification were realistic. In addition, the data bank provided a solid basis for further system analysis.

TABLE E.1 Most Probable Maximum VSWR and Maximum VSWR at F_{LOW} (5.0 GHz)

Beamport	Most probable maximum VSWR	Maximum VSWR
1	3:1	3.3:1
4	2.8:1	4.3:1
5	2.9:1	4.3:1
8	3:1	3.6:1

TABLE E.2 Most Probable Array-Factor Gain

Frequency (GHz)	Outer beamports (dB)	Center beamports (dB)
5.0	4.9, 5.0	1.6, 1.7
6.8	5.5, 5.7	3.4, 3.1
8.5	6.0, 5.9	3.6, 3.9
13.9	7.6, 7.6	6.0, 6.0
18.0	5.0, 5.0	7.5, 7.3

TABLE E.3 Most Probable Total Insertion Loss

Frequency (GHz)	Outer beamports (dB)	Center beamports (dB)
5.0	3.8, 3.6	6.5, 6.5
6.8	3.0, 2.9	5.5, 5.2
8.5	2.4, 2.3	5.0, 4.9
13.9	1.3, 1.2	2.8, 2.8
18.0	2.7, 2.8	1.4, 1.4

TABLE E.4 Electrical Length Center Ports (degrees at 18 GHz)

Lens S/N	BP 4 to AP 5*	BP 5 to AP 4
71	2044	2040
72	2026	2031
74	2031	2026
76	2020	2032
77	2020	2032
78	2025	2017
81	2031	2024
82	2034	2029

*BP is an abbreviation for beamport; AP is an abbreviation for arrayport.

Average electrical length = 2029°

Standard deviation: ± 7.1°

TABLE E.5 Standard Deviation: Array-Factor Gain (dB) (15 Samples)

Frequency (GHz)	Outer beamports	Center beamports
5.0	0.25, 0.25	0.39, 0.32
6.8	0.47, 0.36	0.57, 0.54
8.5	0.10, 0.11	0.39, 0.22
13.9	1.60, 1.55	1.77, 1.80
18.0	0.45, 0.60	0.32, 0.42

TABLE E.6 Standard Deviation: Total Insertion Loss (dB) (15 Samples)

Frequency (GHz)	Outer beamports	Center beamports
5.0	0.26, 0.25	0.28, 0.31
6.8	0.40, 0.31	0.48, 0.48
8.5	0.10, 0.11	0.17, 0.21
13.9	0.17, 0.25	0.59, 0.65
18.0	0.38, 0.56	0.30, 0.36

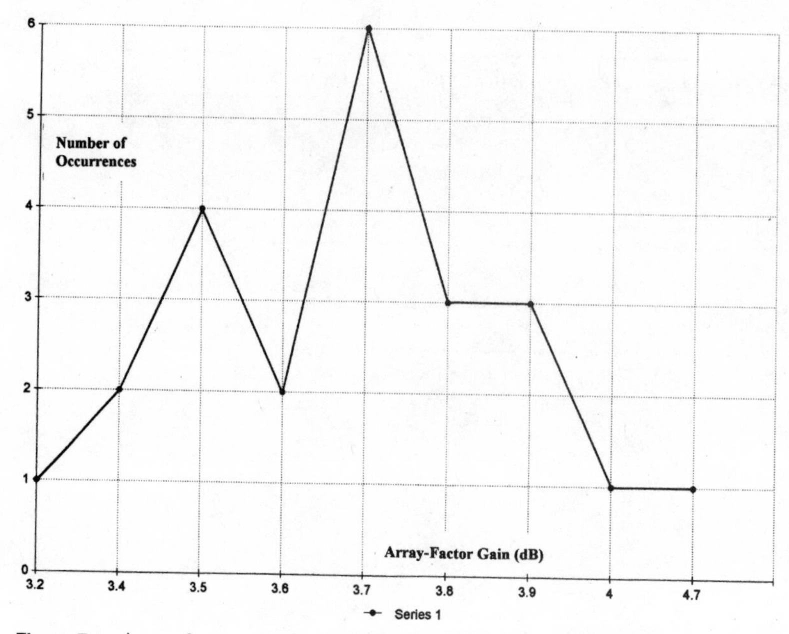

Figure E.1 Array-factor gain histogram (center port, 8.5 GHz).

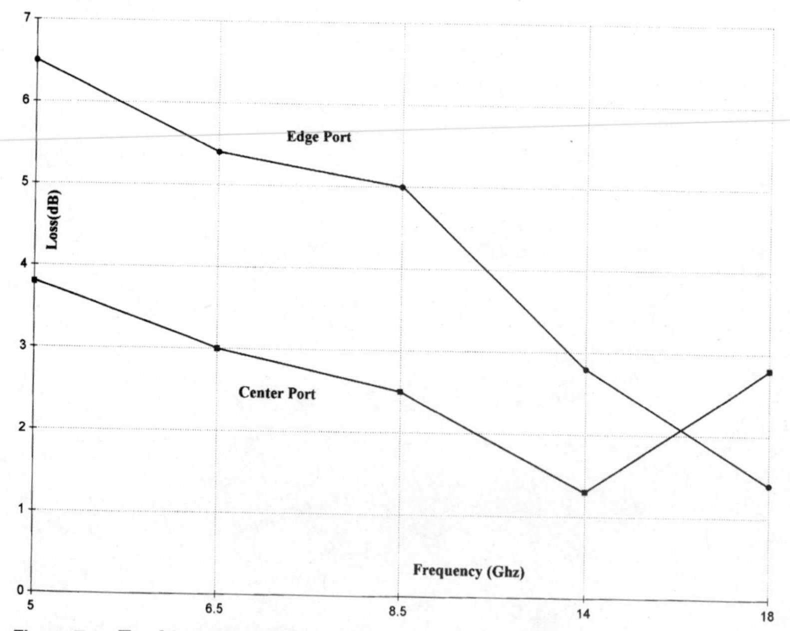

Figure E.2 Total insertion loss vs. frequency (center and edge ports).

Appendix

Saturated Drive and Beam Patterns

F.1 Introduction

In describing the transmit beam patterns, it was noted that they are nearly the same as the receive patterns, except for slightly higher side lobes and somewhat broader beams. This appendix describes why the changes occur from receive to transmit.

F.2 Saturated Drive

In the text, a coupler was inserted between the near-center lens output and the input to the power amplifier to assure nearly saturated drive.

Figure F.1 shows a simplified schematic, illustrating how drive is established for the power amplifier. A single input driver is placed ahead of the lens and the power is then fanned out to the power amplifiers. Each input lens port provides a unique distribution resulting in varying degrees of saturation.

Figure F.2 shows a typical transfer curve for the power amplifier. The established input drive power results in a given power output. As the drive is increased beyond linear operation, the output power increases until, finally, saturated power results (peak of the curve). Ideally, the drive level is set slightly beyond linear operation (i.e., 1 or 2 dB into compression).

Figure F.3 shows a typical beam pattern in the receive mode. The dashed pattern was obtained during transmit (nonlinear) operation.

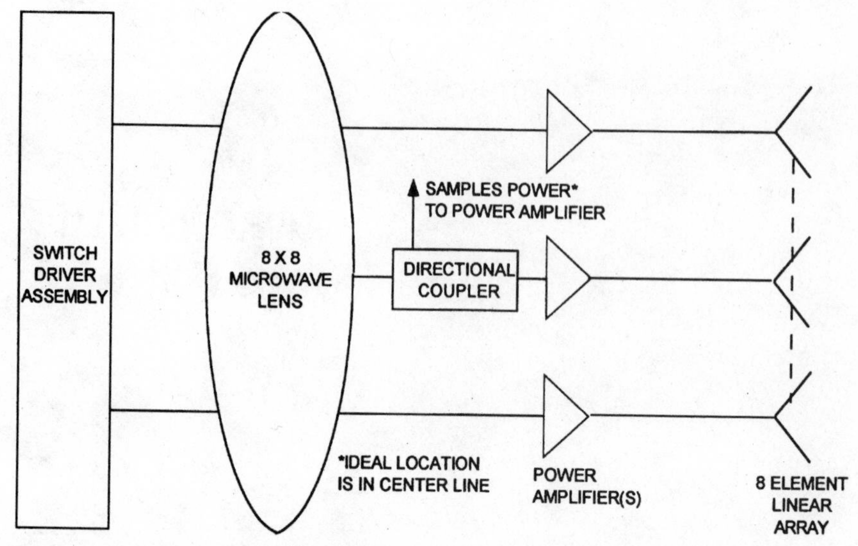

Figure F.1 Power drive setup (simplified).

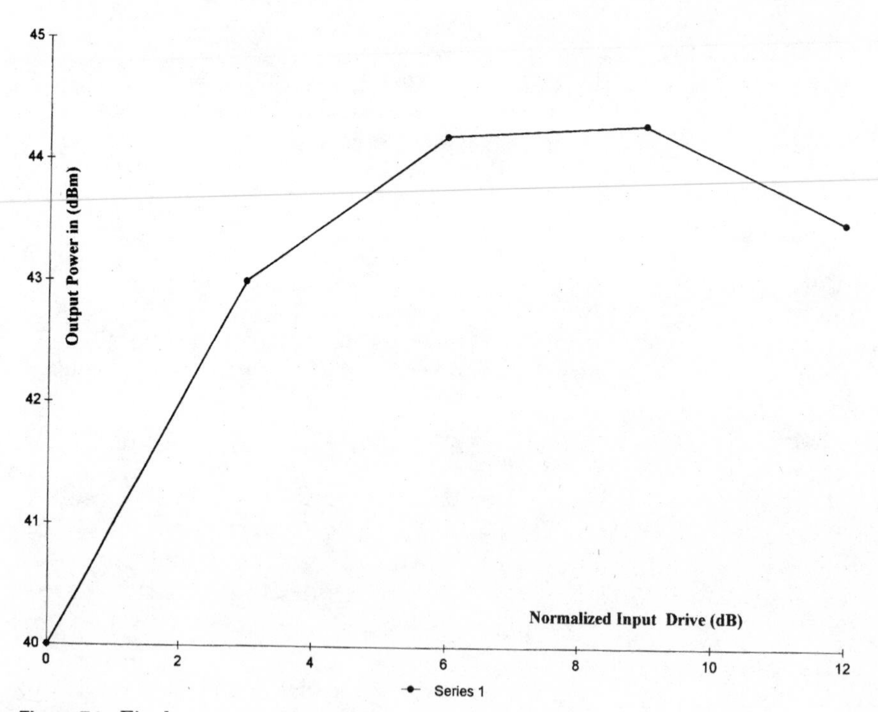

Figure F.2 Final power amplifier transfer curve (normalized).

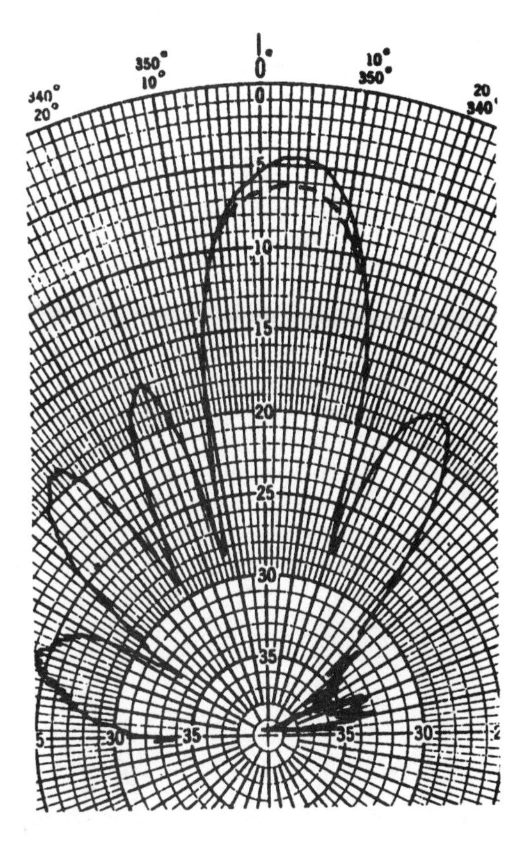

Figure F.3 Receive and transmit (dashed) beam patterns. (*Courtesy of Raytheon Company*)

The effect of power amplifier compression is to reduce the peak beam pattern amplitude by approximately the compression level, yielding a broader 3-dB beamwidth with an apparent increase in side lobe levels. The resulting effect on the beam patterns is approximate because only one coupler is used to sample the drive level. Other final amplifiers will be driven to different outputs, depending upon the lens transfer characteristics, which in turn depend on which beam-port is used as the input.

Appendix G

A Typical Patent Sequence

G.1 Introduction

The patenting process consists of four steps:

- Preparing the disclosure
- Working with the patent attorney
- Supporting the patent claims
- Receiving the patent

Each of these steps involves different skills.

G.2 Preparing a Disclosure

The disclosure is written by the inventor(s). At a minimum, it should provide

- A statement of the problem
- A description of the invention
- How it solves the problem
- New (unique) features of the invention
- Potential applications

Each of these items should be delineated in clear, concise wording that can be readily understood by a patent attorney (not a design specialist). Photographs, figures, and charts should be used liberally, along with text, to describe and discuss the invention.

G.3 Working with the Patent Attorney

The patent attorney and technical support staff will then review the submitted disclosure. Questions from them requesting clarification will follow. Also, other patents similar to the submitted disclosure will be forwarded to the inventor for review. Identification of new or novel features in the disclosure versus prior design art will be requested.

When it is determined that the material is suitable for a patent, a formal disclosure for submission to the U.S. Patent Office will be prepared by the attorney. Here, the inventor may be asked for additional clarifications. Upon completion of the disclosure, it will be submitted to the inventor for review. Here, for the first time, the inventor will be reviewing a document that contains the essence of the invention written in legal language (Fig. G.1) with claims (Fig. G.2) that the patent will hold.

4,132,995

3

support structure 12 and a cover 46, here made of Teflon-Fiberglas having a dielectric constant of 2.54, to the housing 30 using conventional screws, not shown. Holes 44, 45, also drilled and tapped, are provided for the coaxial connector 31. When assembled the edges of the conductive sheets 14 are in electrical and mechanical contact with the edge 37 (including mounting flanges 35, 36) formed about the periphery of the cavity 33. It is noted, therefore, that a portion of such mounting edge 37 (i.e. a portion of flange 36) provides an electrical connection or short circuit across the narrow portion 20 of the slot 16 formed along the back edge 34 of the dielectric support structure. A deflection plate 50 is machined into the housing 30 to form one surface of the cavity 33. Such deflection plate 50 makes an acute angle with the dielectric support structure 12, here a 45 degree angle, as shown. The deflection plate 50 is disposed beneath the wide portion 22 of the slot 16, as shown. In particular, the edge 52 of the deflection plate 50 extends parallel to the back edge 34 of the dielectric support structure 12 and such edge 52 is displaced from such back edge 34 a length, E, here in the order of 2.4 inches. The depth of the cavity, D, is here 0.5 inch.

It is noted that, when assembled, the antenna element 10 is a box-shaped structure having an outside depth of about 0.75 inch. Such antenna element 10 is flush-mountable within the metal conductive surface 56 of a vehicle 58 (FIGS. 4 and 5). The boresight axis 60 of the antenna element 10 is orthogonal to the planar surface of the antenna element 10 (i.e. orthogonal to the planar surfaces of the dielectric support structure 12) as shown in FIG. 4. The conductive surface 56 of the vehicle 58 provides a finite ground plane for the antenna element 10.

4

parallel to the feed line 18 and the plane of the support 12. It is also noted that the feed 18 radiates energy along the direction of boresight axis 60 because such feed 18 may be considered as a monopole radiating element where the bottom portion of the cavity substantially serves as a reflector for such monopole radiating element. The electric field component of this radiated energy is also parallel to the feed 18 and the plane of the support 12. The time delay caused by the separation between the feed 18 and the discontinuity in the slot 16 causes a phase difference between the fields radiated by such feed 18 and the slot 16. The electrical length separating the feed 18 and the discontinuity is less than $\lambda c/2$ where λc is the nominal operating, free space, wavelength of the antenna element 10. Preferably such electrical length is in the order of $\lambda c/4$. Here the separation between the feed 18 and the discontinuity in the slot 16 is in the order of $\lambda c/4$ where λc is 7.866 inches. The vectorial addition of the fields radiated by the slot 16 (and deflected by the deflection plate 50) and radiated by the feed 18 results in antenna 10 producing a cardioid-shaped radiation pattern. A typical radiation pattern for such antenna element 10 is shown in FIG. 6. Such pattern is measured in a plane orthogonal to the support structure and parallel to the feed 18. It is noted that such radiation pattern is cardioid-shaped. Referring to FIG. 5, a pair of antenna elements 10 is shown mounted to opposite sides of an aircraft 58 for use in a left/right amplitude sensing system 62. It is noted that the antenna elements 10 are flush-mounted with the metal conductive surface 56 of the vehicle 58 (FIG. 4) and further that because the antenna elements 10 are grounded to the conductive surface of the aircraft 58, such antenna elements 10 are not subject to damage from lightning

Figure G.1 Typical patent text.

only by the spirit and scope of the appended claims.

What is claimed is:

1. A radio frequency antenna, comprising:

(a) a dielectric support structure;

(b) a conductive sheet having a flared, discontinuous slot formed therein, such slot being disposed on one surface of the support structure;

(c) a feed for coupling radio frequency energy across a narrow portion of the flared slot; and

(d) a housing having: a cavity with conductive walls formed therein, the dielectric support structure being mounted to the housing to provide a cover for such cavity; and a deflection plate forming a wall of such cavity, such deflection plate being disposed at an acute angle with respect to the dielectric support structure and beneath a wide portion of the slot.

2. The radio frequency antenna recited in claim 1 wherein the dielectric support structure is planar and the deflection plate makes a forty-five degree angle with the plane of the support. 5

3. The radio frequency antenna recited in claim 1 wherein a conductor is disposed across the narrow portion of the slot. 10

4. The radio frequency antenna recited in claim 3 wherein the feed is disposed between the conductor and a discontinuity region of the slot.

5. The radio frequency antenna recited in claim 4 wherein the feed is formed on a surface of the support structure. 15

6. The radio frequency antenna recited in claim 1 wherein the feed is displaced from the discontinuity

4,132,995

Figure G.2 Typical patent claims.

G.4 Working with the U.S. Patent Office

Upon receipt and review of the disclosure, the Patent Office will review and return it with comments and other relatable patents, possibly including non-English patents. Again, the inventor will be asked to comment on the new or novel features of the disclosure versus prior art. And, since claims represent a very important part of any patent (because they limit infringement), a dialogue is desirable in an effort to preserve the claims. The disclosure will then be updated and resubmitted for patent consideration.

G.5 Granting of the Patent

Upon concurrence of the validity of the patenting material and the resolution of claims to be appended to the forthcoming patent, a patent will be issued (Fig. G.3).

Be prepared for the full cycle (from the initially submitted application to the patent) to take two to three years.

United States Patent [19] [11] **4,132,995**
Monser [45] **Jan. 2, 1979**

[54] **CAVITY BACKED SLOT ANTENNA**

[75] Inventor: **George J. Monser**, Goleta, Calif.

[73] Assignee: **Raytheon Company**, Lexington, Mass.

[21] Appl. No.: **846,740**

[22] Filed: **Oct. 31, 1977**

[51] **Int. Cl.**^{2} **H01Q 1/28**; H01Q 13/18
[52] **U.S. Cl.** **343/767**; 343/789
[58] **Field of Search** 343/705, 708, 767, 768, 343/769, 789

[56] **References Cited**

U.S. PATENT DOCUMENTS

2,885,676 5/1959 **Baldwin** 343/767

Primary Examiner—Eli Lieberman

Attorney, Agent, or Firm—Richard M. Sharkansky; Joseph D. Pannone

[57] **ABSTRACT**

A radio frequency antenna having a flared, discontinuous slot formed on one surface of a dielectric support structure and a feed formed on the opposite surface of such structure. The feed is disposed across a narrow portion of the slot. A housing having a cavity formed therein is provided. The dielectric support is disposed on the housing over the cavity. The cavity has a conductive wall, or deflective plate, disposed beneath a wide portion of the slot. The effects of the feed and the slot-deflection plate combine to provide a flush-mountable antenna having a cardioid-shaped radiation pattern.

8 Claims, 6 Drawing Figures

Figure G.3 Typical patent cover sheet. (*Courtesy of Raytheon Company*)

Once issued, the patent protects the invention. It will also provide recognition of the contribution and possibly advancement (within the corporate structure).

Appendix

H

Antenna Details

This appendix provides additional data for the antennas described in the text. Some applications are included to illustrate the versatility of the designs.

H.1 Microwave Array and Adaptation

Figure H.1 shows the microwave array (Monser and Roy, 1982) illustrated in the text. Details of the finished coaxial-to-waveguide transition extracted from patent number 4,353,074 are shown in Fig. H.2.

Figure H.1 Microwave array. *(Courtesy of Raytheon Company)*

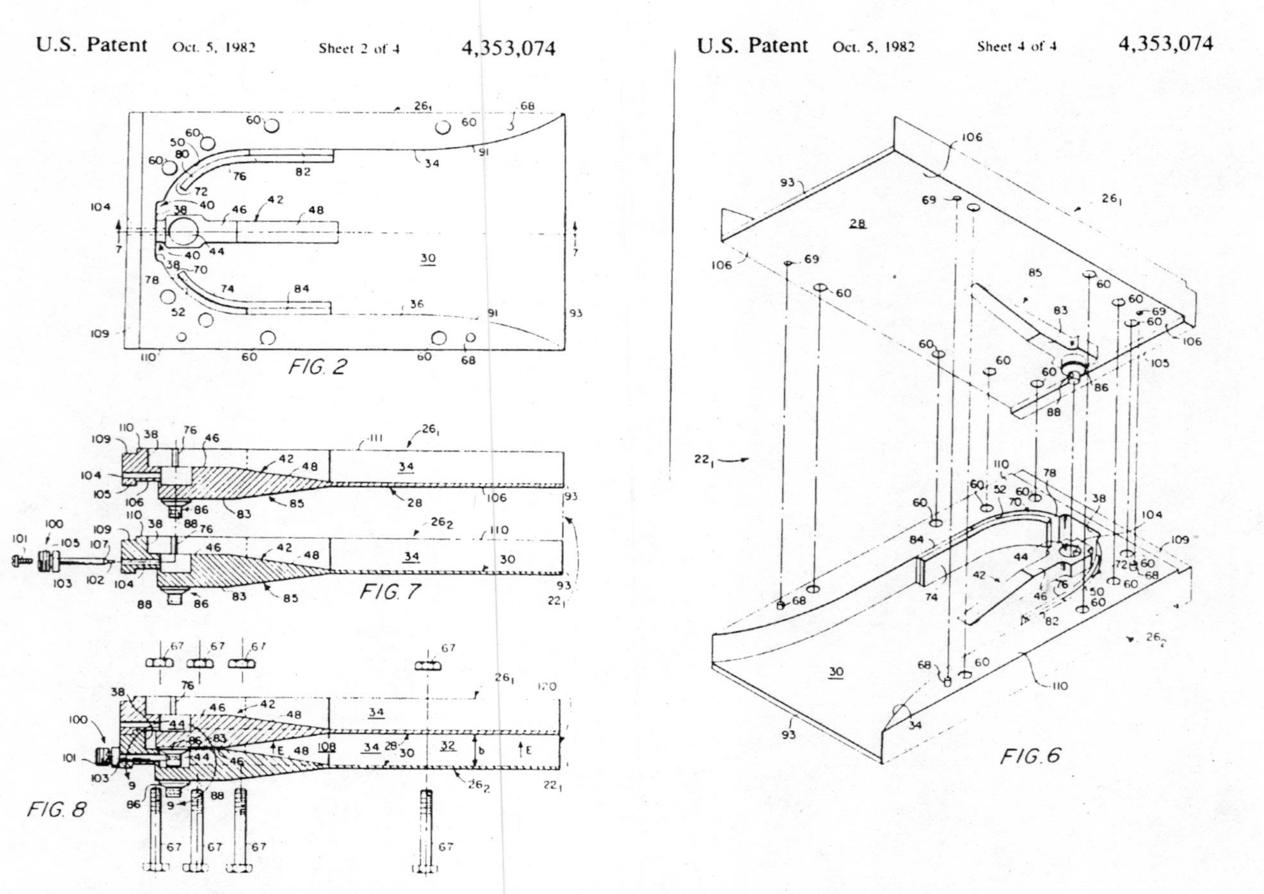

Figure H.2 Assembly and coaxial line to waveguide transition (patent no. 4,353,074). *(Courtesy of Raytheon Company)*

Figure H.3 Receive array without polarizer. (*Courtesy of Raytheon Company*)

Figure H.3 shows the array installed for use as a receive array. The array polarizer is not shown. Here, full sector coverage is required with minimum shadowing by the low band, dual-spiral antenna.

Figure H.4 shows a bottom view of the array used to receive with the polarizer installed. The air gaps between pairs of polarizer sheets are not required, but are used so that nearly identical receive and transmit polarization characteristics will result. In all respects the designs are identical. Shown here also is the polarization-grid spacing in the end wraparounds that are less than optimum due to space constraints.

Figure H.5 shows an experimental setup using the microwave array and lens. The purpose of this test is to validate that −40 dB nulls could be achieved by feeding adjacent lens ports 180° out of phase.

Figure H.6 shows three elements of a shortened version (Monser, 1985) of the microwave array.

Figure H.7 shows a short version of the array used to feed a reflector assembly to achieve narrower H-plane patterns (for the array element) and improved gain.

Figure H.8 presents the printed-circuit, four-element notch array in two holding fixtures for power test. The aluminum fixture (left) is ideal for heat-sinking by clamping the opposite smooth side to an aluminum block. The right fixture is made of G-10 dielectric, which

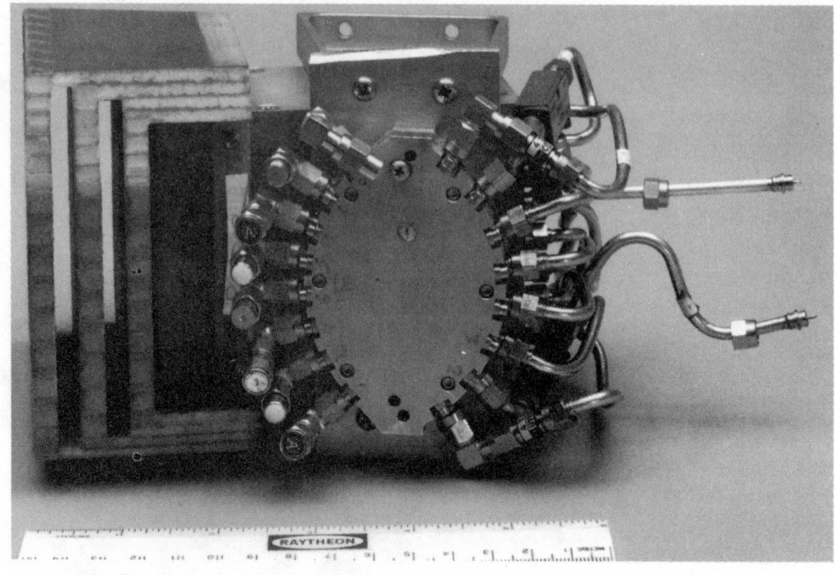

Figure H.4 Receive array with polarizer (bottom view, same spacing as transmit polarizer). (*Courtesy of Raytheon Company*)

Figure H.5 Null test using microwave array and lens. (*Courtesy of Raytheon Company*)

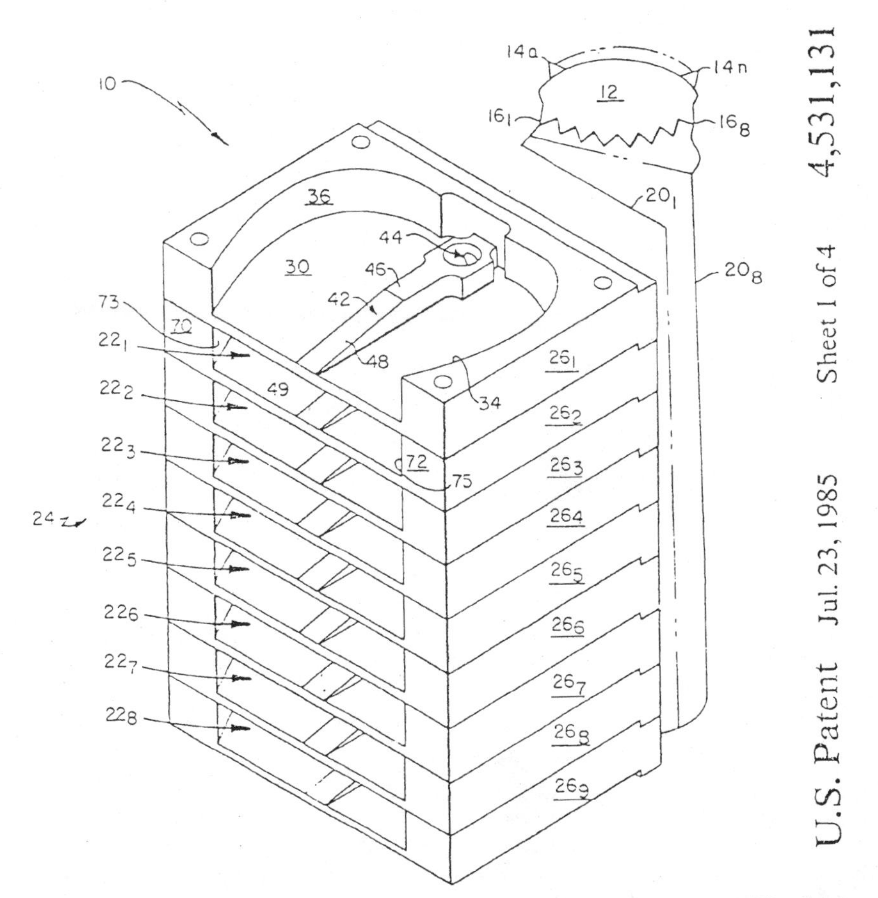

Figure H.6 Microwave array (short version—6 to 18 GHz model). (*Courtesy of Raytheon Company*)

Figure H.7 Short microwave array feeding a reflector. (*Courtesy of Raytheon Company*)

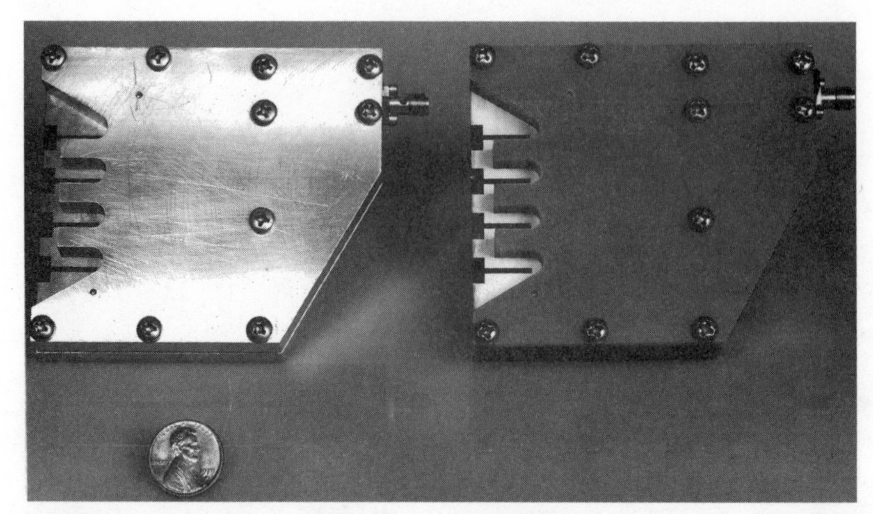

Figure H.8 Printed-circuit subarrays in power test fixtures. (*Courtesy of Raytheon Company*)

Figure H.9 Dual-polarized array, test setup. (*Courtesy of Raytheon Company*)

yields poor heat transfer and thus results in maximum thermal stress to the stripline circuit.

Figure H.9 shows the test setup used to check the dual-polarized array (Monser, 1982). The array is composed of horn elements similar

Figure H.10 Five-element, dual-polarized array (first model with suspended subarrays on horn centerlines), improved design. (*Courtesy of Raytheon Company*)

to the microwave array. The adjoining walls are partially removed allowing the stripline, four-element notch array's installation.

Figure H.10 shows an experimental five-element, dual-polarized array (Roy and Monser, 1987). Here, electrically isolated stripline assemblies, positioned on the centerline of each horn element are used, providing nearly identical phase centers for the horn and stripline assemblies for improved circular polarization when fed through 90° apart to each dual-polarized array element.

H.2 Other Designs

Figure H.11 shows an 18-element horn array used in the AN/SLQ-32 system.

Figure H.12 shows the AN/SLQ-32 mounted for test in an anechoic chamber. This system complex is illustrated in this book's Introduction as a U.S. Navy installation.

Figure H.13 shows a printed-notch antenna mounted over a shallow cavity (Monser, 1979). Gain and VSWR for the printed notch over the cavity are given in Figs. H.14 and H.15. The design reported by Monser in 1986, showed that, as a receive antenna, the unit per-

Figure H.11 AN/SLQ-32, transmit array. (*Courtesy of Raytheon Company*)

Figure H.12 AN/SLQ-32 system in test chamber. (*Courtesy of Raytheon Company*)

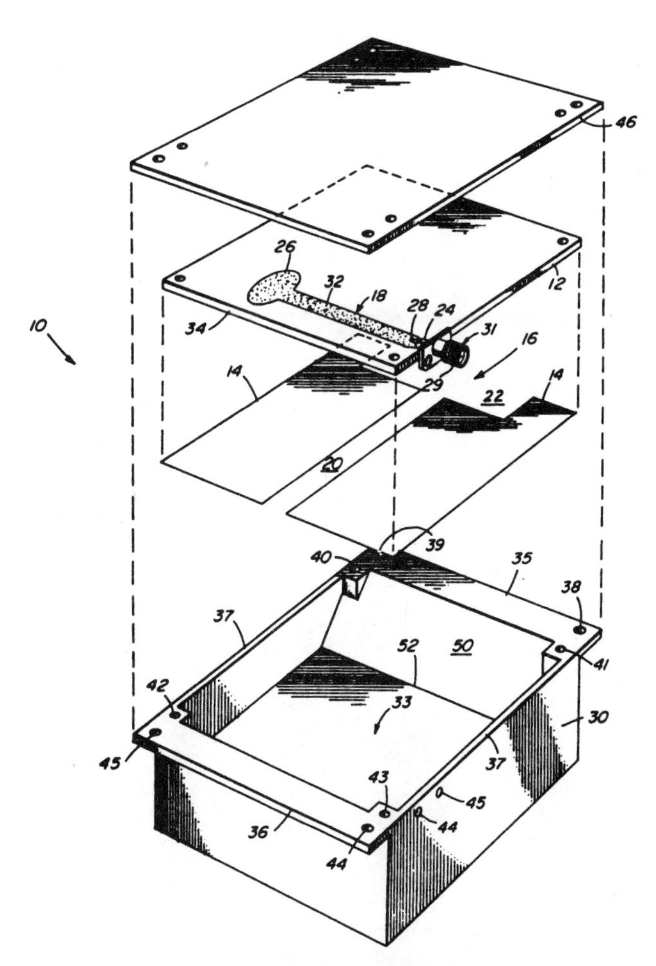

United States Patent [19]

Monser

[11] **4,132,995**

[45] **Jan. 2, 1979**

Figure H.13 Printed notch over cavity. (*Courtesy of Raytheon Company*)

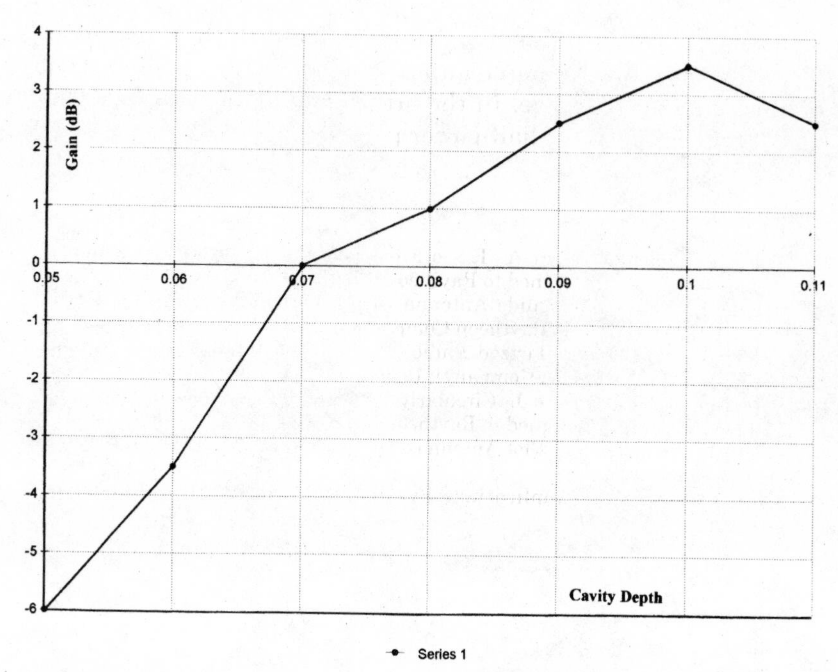

Figure H.14 Micronotch gain vs. cavity depth in wavelengths.

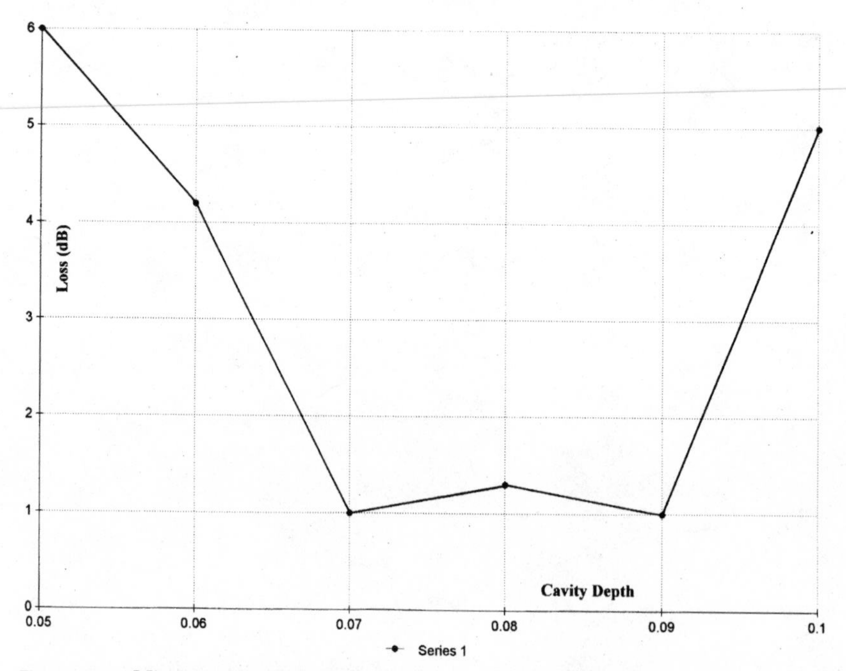

Figure H.15 Micronotch VSWR loss vs. cavity depth in wavelengths.

formed well over greater than an octave in bandwidth. Patterns in the plane defined by the notch input line (principal polarization plane) afforded 180° coverage. In the orthogonal plane, coverage was typically 80° to 90° between half-power points.

References

Monser, George J., and Roy, Albert A., Radio Frequency Ridged Waveguide Antenna, Patent Number 4,353,074 (assigned to Raytheon Company), 1982.

Monser, George J., Ridged Waveguide Antenna with Concave-Shaped Walls, Patent Number 4,531,131 (assigned to Raytheon Company), 1985.

Monser, George J., Circularly Polarized Radio Frequency Antenna, Patent Number 4,353,072 (assigned to Raytheon Company), 1982.

Roy, Albert A., and Monser, George J., Circularly Polarized Radio Frequency Antenna, Patent Number 4,672,384 (assigned to Raytheon Company), 1987.

Monser, George J., Cavity-Backed Slot Antenna, Patent Number 4,132,995 (assigned to Raytheon Company), 1979.

Monser, George J., Antenna Applications Symposium, USAF/U.Ill., Champaign, Illinois, 1986.

Appendix

I

Design Notes for a Log-periodic Antenna

I.1 Introduction

The log-periodic antenna belongs to the class of frequency-independent antennas. This antenna has appeared in a variety of forms both as planar structures and as pyramidal structures. Radiating elements that have appeared in practical designs include: thin, cylindrical elements; uniform width elements; saw-tooth elements; and thin elements end-loaded to foreshorten into a more compact size. All of the designs have common design techniques.

I.2 Design

Figure I.1 shows a photograph of a printed-circuit log-periodic antenna. On the other side of the board, the circuit elements are identical but flipped to a mirror image. The simplest feed is to bond a coaxial line to one side as shown and then to connect the center conductor to the circuit on the opposite side at the apex, yielding an infinite-balun feed. This configuration is useful for multioctave designs.

The design starts by selecting the size of the largest element, farthest from the apex, to extend one-half wavelength end-to-end (i.e., includes the mirror image) at the lowest frequency of operation. At times, the largest element is set 10 to 20 percent larger for better gain at the lowest frequency where space and need exist.

Next, the elements are located shorter distances from the apex than the largest element using a constant multiplier, typically 0.8. For example, the next largest element is 0.8 times the distance for the

Figure I.1 Printed-circuit log-periodic antenna.

Figure I.2 Pyramidal log-periodic antenna (end elements foreshortened).

largest element with the layout continued until the apex is reached. Frequently, the smallest element is made into a triangle for convenience, as shown. The element lengths are shortened by the same multiplier, taken here as 0.8.

Figure I.2 shows the extension of the design to a pyramidal structure. Typically, the planar designs yield 6 to 7 dB gain, while the pyramidal units yield 8 to 10 dB. There is a limit on the separation angle, which is reached when the front-to-back ratio in the antenna pattern falls below what is considered acceptable. Here, a separation angle of about 50° has been found to yield acceptable patterns and VSWR under 3/1 over multioctave bandwidth.

In the layout for the elements, the spreading angle can be chosen as design parameter. Here, separation angles from 45° to 60° are typical. The smaller angles yield a larger antenna with somewhat improved over-the-band performance.

Common methods for feeding the antenna include using an infinite balun (as noted earlier), using twin lead mounted along the centerline to bisect the separation angle, and using coaxial line in place of the twin lead and tapering the coaxial shield to form a two-line feed. Except for the last method, the other techniques require a transformer for best performance. For the infinite balun, the transformer can be built in quarter-wave sections within the coaxial line stepping down from 150 Ω (typical) to 50 Ω. For the twin lead, a transformer step-up from 150 Ω (typical) to 300 Ω is needed.

I.3 Concluding Remarks

In addition to the linearly polarized log-periodic antenna, other forms of frequency-independent antennas have found wide use. The frontpiece shows a VHF conical log-spiral type used to form circular polarization over a hemisphere over several octaves bandwidth.

Glossary

anechoic chamber A lined, RF absorber chamber used in antenna testing.

antenna pattern The electric field or power response of an antenna defining the coverage.

ANA Automatic network analyzer, used in testing antennas.

aperture Antenna structure through which the electromagnetic wave flows.

array-factor gain The gain calculated for a lens when feeding unity-gain antenna elements.

axial-ratio The ratio of the two orthogonal fields for an elliptically polarized wave. Usually expressed in dB.

balun An abbreviation for balanced-to-unbalanced transformer.

bank of data A set of data.

boresight Central axis perpendicular to the antenna face or radiating structure.

breadboard antenna A simply constructed rough model of an antenna including the critical elements of the design.

circular polarization Term used to describe the electromagnetic wave when it consists of two equal-amplitude orthogonal fields separated in time by 90°.

coupling A measure of the power or field intensity appearing at an element due to exciting a reference element. A direct measure can be obtained by sending input to one element and measuring the output of the second element.

dielectric Nonmetallic parts of an antenna.

directive gain The ratio of 4Π-steradians to the product of the angular dimensions of the antenna beam (without taking losses into account).

director An element placed ahead of the antenna to improve gain and sharpen the pattern when used with a dipole antenna.

dual-polarized An electromagnetic wave consisting of two, approximately equal, orthogonal components purposely formed.

elliptically polarized An electromagnetic wave consisting of two unequal orthogonal components time-phased other than 90°. Either condition suffices.

empirical Type of physical adjustments made to the physical model in an orderly process to achieve results.

fallout The resulting narrowing of antenna choices through the process of elimination.

free-space conditions Tests conducted without interfering structures present.

gain The increase in radiation intensity due to confining the radiation to less than 4Π-steradians (that resulting from a point source).

gain hole A dropout either in antenna pattern coverage or when swept in frequency over the band.

hard model A physical assembly of the antenna.

implicit requirements Those not in the specification but that are dictated by the system.

kW kilowatt of power (i.e., 1000 watts).

linear gain A measure of the increase in radiation intensity for a linearly polarized wave compared to a point source radiation.

matrix A detailing of test and evaluation limits.

MIL-HDBK-216 Military Standardization Handbook, describing RF transmission lines and fittings, available through the Defense Supply Agency, Washington, DC.

modeling The building of physical models of the antenna.

moding An undesirable change in the propagating field within a waveguide to other than the single dominant mode (i.e., a breakup of the dominant mode into more than one mode).

most probable All values appearing between 1-Σ limits assuming a Gaussian distribution.

paper design Analysis and notes pertaining to the antenna preceding any hard modeling.

platform The structure upon which the system is mounted (e.g., aircraft, ship, etc.).

pod A cannister mounted on aircraft to house equipment outside the mainframe.

polarization purity A measure of how well the field is confined to a single linear dimension.

principal plane A plane either aligned or orthogonal to the primary polarization of the antenna.

probe A transitional part inside a wavelength to convert the coaxial input (TEM) to the waveguide field (e.g., TE-mode).

reflector An antenna element placed behind the antenna to improve gain and sharpen the pattern. Used with dipole antennas, the director is slightly longer than the dipole.

ridged waveguide Waveguide with structures inside the guide to reduce the cutoff frequency and extend the bandwidth.

rms root mean square.

saturated drive A condition in which the output power and the input power are not linearly related. Here, when the power amplifier is excited at low input the output power changes 1 dB for every change of 1 dB of drive. Approaching the maximum output available, compression occurs (nonlinear operation).

sensitivity A measure of the response of the antenna to the incident field (closely related to the antenna gain).

simulated environment A near replica of the actual environment in a controlled test.

single registration In stripline, the pattern appears on only one of the two dielectric surfaces inside the stripline.

split-tapered balun The transition from coaxial line to two-line transmission achieved by tapering away the coaxial outer conductor.

squint Relocating the antenna beam maximum off the boresight direction.

stripline Construction in which the active conductor is sandwiched between two parallel metallic plates. For microwaves the spacing of the plates is under $\frac{1}{8}$ inch (typically).

subarray A building block in which several elements are used to form one array element.

taper Transitional flow. For example, in ridged waveguide the ridges commence at the probe and are gradually thinned down approaching the aperture.

traps Structures inside the waveguide antenna that reduce unwanted side-wall currents.

trimming Successive cuts made to the antenna. For example, a dipole can be made slightly longer than the design length and then shortened to achieve resonant performance.

tuning Adjustments to achieve resonant operation. Generally used with small antennas such as whips and loops to realize maximum response.

tweaking Physical adjustments made to the test model during design tests to achieve the optimum performance.

VSWR Voltage standing wave ratio. To measure VSWR, a probe is used to sample the field along the transmission line over lengths exceeding one-half wavelength. The maximum-to-minimum response is the VSWR.

whip An electrically short vertical antenna with physical dimensions under one-quarter wavelength in size. For example, at 100 MHz the wavelength is about 10 ft and a typical whip is under 2.5 ft in height.

References

Bond, D. S., *Radio Direction Finders,* McGraw-Hill, New York, 1944.

Brown, G. H., and Woodward, O. M., Jr., "Experimentally Determined Radiation Characteristics of Conical and Triangular Antennas," *RCA Review,* December 1952, pp. 425–452.

Hacking, C. A., et al., "Man/Machine Design of a Broadband Microwave Circular Polarizer," *Second International Conference on System Sciences,* Hawaii (report of work performed at Stanford Research Institute in 1966), 1969.

Lerner, D. S., "A Wave Polarization Converter for Circular Polarization," *Trans. IEEE,* AP-13: January 1965, pp. 3–7.

Ludwig, Arthur C., "Mutual Coupling, Gain, and Directivity of an Array of Two Identical Antennas," *IEEE Transactions,* AP-24:837–841, 1976.

Monser, George J., Antenna Applications Symposium, USAF/U.Ill., Champaign, Illinois, 1986.

Monser, George J., Cavity-Backed Slot Antenna, Patent Number 4,132,995 (assigned to Raytheon Company), 1979.

Monser, George J., Circularly Polarized Radio Frequency Antenna, Patent Number 4,353,072 (assigned to Raytheon Company), 1982.

Monser, George J., "Measure Antenna Gain Without a Test Range," *Microwave & RF,* September 1994, pp. 113–114.

Monser, George J., Ridged Waveguide Antenna with Concave-Shaped Walls, Patent Number 4,531,131 (assigned to Raytheon Company), 1985.

Monser, George J., and Roy, Albert A., Radio Frequency Ridged Waveguide Antenna, Patent Number 4,353,074 (assigned to Raytheon Company), 1982.

Roy, Albert A., and Monser, George J., Circularly Polarized Radio Frequency Antenna, Patent Number 4,672,384 (assigned to Raytheon Company), 1987.

Index

ABOUT THE AUTHOR

George J. Monser, P. E., is a consulting engineer in Las Vegas, Nevada. He has more than 35 years of experience in antenna design and spent many of those years as a design engineer with Raytheon. Monser is author of more than 30 technical papers dealing with a variety of antennas and holds 18 patents in the field. He earned a BSEE from Cornell and an MSEE from West Virginia University, where he was also a member of the faculty. He is a registered professional engineer, and a life member of the IEEE.